Number SENSE

Simple Effective Number Sense Experiences

Grades 1–2

Alistair McIntosh

Barbara Reys

Robert Reys

DALE SEYMOUR PUBLICATIONS®

Project Editor: Joan Gideon

Production Coordinator: Leanne Collins

Art: Rachel Gage

Cover Design: Lynda Banks

Text Design: Nancy Benedict

Published by Dale Seymour Publications®, an imprint of the Alternative Publishing Group of Addison-Wesley Publishing Company.

Order Number DS21800

ISBN 1-57232-261-6

This book is printed on recycled paper.

2 3 4 5 6 7 8 9 10-ML-00 99 98 97

CONTENTS

Introduction v

SECTION 1   *Exploring Estimation 1*

EXPERIENCE 1   *About How Many Cans? 3*

EXPERIENCE 2   *Thumbs Up or Down? 8*

EXPERIENCE 3   *About How Many Do You See? 13*

EXPERIENCE 4   *Are There More? 18*

EXPERIENCE 5   *About How Many Will Fit? 23*

EXPERIENCE 6   *How Many Pattern Blocks? 28*

SECTION 2   *Exploring Measurement 33*

EXPERIENCE 7   *Time Out 35*

EXPERIENCE 8   *How Long Is a Handful? 40*

EXPERIENCE 9   *Human Balance 44*

EXPERIENCE 10   *How Much Does It Hold? 48*

EXPERIENCE 11   *Numbers on a Line 51*

SECTION 3   *Exploring Mental Computation 55*

EXPERIENCE 12   *Will You Do It in Your Head? 57*

EXPERIENCE 13   *Today's Target 64*

EXPERIENCE 14   *Adding Compatibles 70*

EXPERIENCE 15   *How Many Dots? 75*

EXPERIENCE 16   *Make It Easier 80*

EXPERIENCE 17   *Skip Counting 85*

EXPERIENCE 18   *Which Path Will You Take? 90*

EXPERIENCE 19   *What Did I Buy? 96*

SECTION 4   *Exploring Multiple Representation 101*

EXPERIENCE 20   *Every Picture Suggests a Story 103*
EXPERIENCE 21   *Finding Equivalent Sums 108*
EXPERIENCE 22   *Making Number Chains 113*
EXPERIENCE 23   *How Could It Happen? 116*
EXPERIENCE 24   *Money Amounts 122*
EXPERIENCE 25   *Number This Name 127*

SECTION 5   *Exploring Number Relationships 131*

EXPERIENCE 26   *Addition and Subtraction Connections 133*
EXPERIENCE 27   *What Number Am I? 138*
EXPERIENCE 28   *My Two Numbers 143*
EXPERIENCE 29   *Finding Triplets 147*
EXPERIENCE 30   *From Here to There 152*

SECTION 6   *Exploring Relative Size 157*

EXPERIENCE 31   *Doubling Numbers 159*
EXPERIENCE 32   *Number Amounts 164*
EXPERIENCE 33   *Pick a Word 169*
EXPERIENCE 34   *Which Number Line? 173*
EXPERIENCE 35   *Where Is It? 178*

INTRODUCTION

Number sense refers to a person's understanding of number concepts, operations, and applications of numbers and operations. It includes the ability and inclination to use this understanding in flexible ways to make mathematical judgments and to develop useful strategies for handling numbers and operations. Number sense results in an expectation that numbers are useful and that mathematics has a certain regularity. A person with good number sense has the ability to use numbers and quantitative methods to communicate, process, and interpret information.

The four-book *Number SENSE: Simple Effective Number Sense Experiences* series is designed to promote thinking and reflection about numbers. The activities help students in primary through middle grades develop number sense through exploring patterns, developing mental-computation skills, understanding different but equivalent representations, establishing benchmarks, recognizing reasonableness, and acquiring estimation skills. Visualization is integral to many activities, as number sense is often developed from visual experiences.

The six sections of this book explore the major components of number sense:

- **Exploring Estimation**
  Working with approximate values to calculate and estimate

- **Exploring Measurement**
  Establishing and working with benchmarks to facilitate estimation

- **Exploring Mental Computation**
  Calculating exact answers mentally, and exploring the thinking that facilitates mental computation

- **Exploring Multiple Representation**
  Identifying and using equivalent forms of numbers and expressions

- **Exploring Number Relationships**
  Exploring number patterns and connections between numbers, and understanding the effect of an operation—addition, subtraction, multiplication, division—on two or more numbers

- **Exploring Relative Size**
  Developing a sense of the size of a number in relation to other numbers, including benchmarks

Each activity falls under one appropriate heading, though most are connected to more than one component of number sense. These interconnections are natural and a reminder that number sense is not a series of disjoint entities but an integration of multidimensional components.

Using the Activities

Each activity is built on the premise that any student can benefit at any time from experiences that encourage them to think about numbers in a sense-making way. The activities can be used in any order, whenever they would be appropriate to anchor, build, and extend students' thinking about numbers in meaningful ways. Most will take from 5 to 15 minutes.

The activities are designed to serve as a source for questions or problems to stimulate thinking and discussion. If the activity is to be presented to the whole class, the activity master may be made into a transparency. Activity masters may also be used to make student copies. When an experience contains more than one activity, begin with the first activity and use the others over a period of time.

Teacher notes explain the intent of each group of activities and suggest ways to present them. The teacher notes contain these components:

- **Number Sense Focus**
  Highlights the main number sense components

- **Number Focus**
  Identifies the types of numbers used in the activity

- **Mathematical Background**
  Describes the rationale or context for the activity, including its connection to different dimensions of number sense—such as relationships of fractions, multiple representation, computational alternatives, and basic facts

- **Using the Activity**
  Offers ideas for preparing students for the activity as well as ways to initiate the experience, questions to raise, and possible directions to take.

- **Solutions**
  Provides answers when appropriate and additional insight for some answers

- **Extending the Activity**
  Suggests teacher-directed extensions or variations as well as extensions for students to explore on their own

The Importance of Number Sense

Current reforms in mathematics education emphasize number sense as it typifies the theme of learning mathematics as a sense-making activity. Like common sense, *number sense* is an elusive term. It has been discussed by mathematics educators, including classroom teachers, curriculum writers, and researchers. Discussions include lists of essential components of number sense (McIntosh, Reys, and Reys, 1992; Resnick, 1989; Sowder and Schappelle, 1989; Sowder, 1992; Willis, 1990), descriptions of students displaying number sense (or lack thereof) (Howden, 1989; Reys, 1991, 1994), and an in-depth theoretical analysis of number sense from a psychological perspective (Greeno, 1991). Number sense is highly personal. It is related to *what* ideas about number have been established as well as to *how* those ideas were established.

The NCTM *Curriculum and Evaluation Standards* sets forth that children with good number sense have well-understood number meanings, understand multiple interpretations and representations of numbers, recognize the relative and absolute magnitude of numbers, appreciate the effect of operations on numbers, and have developed a system of personal benchmarks.

Number sense exhibits itself in various ways as the learner engages in mathematical thinking. It is an important underlying theme as the learner chooses, develops, and uses computational methods, including written computation, mental computation, calculators, and estimation. The creation and application of algorithms calls upon facets of number sense such as decomposition, recomposition, and understanding number properties. When paper-and-pencil algorithms and calculator algorithms are used, number sense is important as answers are evaluated for reasonableness.

The acquisition of number sense is gradual, commencing long before formal schooling begins. Number sense is often evident at an early age as children try to make sense of numbers. However, growing older does not necessarily ensure either the development or use of even the most primitive notions of number sense. Indeed, although many young children exhibit creative and sometimes efficient strategies for operating with numbers, attention to formal algorithms may actually deter use of informal methods. As students' technical knowledge of mathematics expands, their range of strategies may narrow.

Learned algorithms become the methods most cherished by many students, as they can be executed without much thought. The reaction of a student when asked whether a calculation seems reasonable is often to recalculate—generally using the same method as before—rather than to reflect on the result in light of the context. The lack of a natural inclination to reconsider a calculation is all too common both in and out of school. When selling three items priced at $2.19 each, a clerk reported a total due of $4.88. When the customer responded that the amount seemed too low, the clerk showed no inclination to reflect on the reasonableness of the result. When pressed, the clerk recalculated the amount due. Only when a different total appeared on the register did the clerk recognize an error. While the method of checking (recalculating) is not being questioned, the lack of reflective reasoning is worrisome.

There is evidence that the context in which mathematical problems are encountered influences a student's thinking. For example, while a student may be comfortable in school with a sum of 514 produced by applying a learned algorithm to the computation of $26 + 38$, the same student in a store will likely demand a reexamination if asked to pay $5.14 for two items priced at 26¢ and 38¢.

Students who are highly skilled at paper-and-pencil computations—often the gauge by which mathematics success is measured—may or may not be developing good number sense. When a student reports that $40 - 36 = 16$ or that $\frac{2}{5} + \frac{3}{7} = \frac{5}{12}$, he or she is attempting to apply a learned algorithm but is not reflecting on the reasonableness of the answer. In fact, much of the recent attention to developing number sense is a reaction to overemphasis on computational, algorithmic procedures.

The degree of number sense needed in the world today is greater than ever. Both students and adults encounter a greater range of numbers (government budgets in the trillions of dollars, athletic events timed to the thousandths of a second), in more varied contexts (including graphs and surveys), and encounter more tools (such as computers and calculators) than a generation ago. It might be said that the possession of number sense is the one major attribute that distinguishes human beings from computers. There is every reason to believe that the twenty-first century will demand an even higher level of number sense.

The Teacher's Role in Developing Number Sense

The breadth and depth of students' number sense will grow as they encounter situations that encourage them to reflect on reasonableness, to think about numbers and operations, and to make flexible use of numbers and operations in a variety of situations. Focusing on number sense encourages students to use common sense and to become involved in making sense of numerical situations. *Sense making* is what number sense is all about.

As a teacher, you play a key role in developing your students' number sense by encouraging them to make sense of situations. As activities are explored, spend plenty of time discussing answers and strategies by focusing on questions such as these:

- How did you get your answer?

- Can you explain it another way?

- Did anyone think about it differently?

When there are wrong answers, find out why. Was it faulty reasoning, a computational error, or something else? Sharing how people—including you—thought about the question or problem provides different dimensions of insight into the solution process.

The activities in this book encourage dialogue among students and teachers. We believe that the success of these activities in promoting sense making will be directly related to the quality of the sharing and exchanging of ideas that occurs in your classroom.

References

Greeno, J. G. "Number Sense as Situated Knowing in a Conceptual Domain." *Journal for Research in Mathematics Education* 22 (1991): 170–218.

Howden, H. "Teaching Number Sense." *The Arithmetic Teacher* 36 (1989): 6–11.

McIntosh, A., B. Reys, and R. Reys. "A Proposed Framework for Examining Basic Number Sense." *For the Learning of Mathematics* 12 (1992): 2–8.

National Council of Teachers of Mathematics. *Curriculum and Evaluation Standards for School Mathematics.* Reston, Va.: National Council of Teachers of Mathematics, 1989.

Resnick, L. B. "Defining, Assessing and Teaching Number Sense." In *Establishing Foundations for Research on Number Sense and Related Topics: Report of a Conference,* eds. J. Sowder and B. Schappelle. San Diego, Calif.: San Diego State University, Center for Research in Mathematics and Science Education, 1989.

Reys, B. J., R. Barger, B. Dougherty, J. Hope, L. Lembke, Z. Markovitz, A. Parmas, S. Reehm, R. Sturdevant, M. Weber, and M. Bruckheimer. *Developing Number Sense in the Middle Grades.* Reston, Va.: National Council of Teachers of Mathematics, 1991.

Reys, B. J. "Promoting Number Sense in Middle Grades." *Mathematics Teaching in the Middle Grades* 1, no. 2 (1994): 114–20.

Sowder, J. T. "Estimation and Number Sense." In *Handbook of Research on Mathematics Teaching and Learning,* ed. D. A. Grouws, 371–89. New York: Macmillan, 1992.

Sowder J. T. and B. P. Schappelle, eds. *Establishing Foundations for Research on Number Sense and Related Topics: Report of a Conference.* San Diego, Calif.: San Diego State University, Center for Research in Mathematics and Science Education, 1989.

Willis, S., ed. *Being Numerate: What Counts?* Hawthorne, Victoria: Australian Council for Educational Research, 1990.

Exploring Estimation

Estimates are useful when exact answers are impossible, unrealistic, or unnecessary. Measurements such as money, length, area, distance, and time are approximations; they can be made more accurate by using a smaller unit, but they are always approximate. Estimation is about producing answers that are close enough to allow for good decisions without making extremely precise measurements or doing elaborate computations.

The first step in developing estimation skill is to learn to recognize whether a particular situation requires an exact answer or an estimate, and the degree of accuracy needed. When timing a slow-cooking casserole, half an hour more or less may not be crucial; with a microwave, seconds matter. Deciding whether to estimate and how closely to estimate promotes and rewards high-level mathematical thinking.

Estimation strategies are quite different from those we employ when an exact answer is needed. One valuable estimation technique is relating the estimate to a referent, or benchmark, that we know—such as the height of one story of a building or the capacity of a milk carton. People with good number sense use a variety of personal benchmarks.

Research has shown that estimation employs mental computation, rewards flexible thinking, challenges students to think about numbers in ways that are meaningful for them, develops an awareness of multiple strategies, encourages a tolerance for error, and builds an appreciation of the power of inexact values in making decisions. The development of estimation skills helps dispel the one-right-answer syndrome often associated with exact computation. Research has also shown that students are often reluctant to estimate because they are more comfortable with exact answers. Thus they are unaware of how powerful estimation can be, both in and out of school.

The activities in this section will help children develop an appreciation for estimation and challenge them to think about what numbers to use and how to use them.

About How Many Cans?

Number Sense Focus

- Estimation
- Multiple representation

Mathematical Background

Children need opportunities to practice a variety of estimation strategies, including looking for patterns and comparing with numerical benchmarks.

Using the Activities

In these activities, children see a group of cans of cat food and estimate the number of cans that are a particular color. This model could be used to explore addition and subtraction in the tens family, but the focus here is on estimation.

1. In Activity 1, tell the children that they will see a row of 10 cans of cat food. The gray cans are for the gray cat, Smudge, and the white cans are for the white cat, Snowball. One at a time, show each row of cans for a few seconds, and ask these questions:

   - Are there more cans for Snowball or for Smudge?

   - About how many cans are there for Smudge? for Snowball?

   If necessary, remind the children that there are 10 cans in all.

Since the focus here is on estimation rather than counting, the class may offer several answers. For example, for the second row of cans, children might give these answers:

- "Most of the cans are gray."

- "All but one are gray."

- "More than half are gray."

If the children conclude that 9 are gray, fine; but emphasize estimation strategies rather than exact answers.

2. In Activity 2, children will see 20 cans in two rows of 10 each.

3. In Activity 3, children will again see 20 cans, but this time some of the cans are for the black cat, Midnight.

Extending the Activities

• •

- The children can make up similar problems for each other, using colored cubes or other objects.

- Invite the children to write all the combinations of two numbers that make 10, all the combinations of two numbers that make 20, and, if they are ready, all the combinations of three numbers that make 20.

About How Many Cans?

1.

2.

3.

4.

5.

6.

About How Many Cans?

1.

2.

3.

4.

5.

About How Many Cans?

1.

2.

3.

4.

5.

EXPERIENCE 2

• •

Thumbs Up or Down?

Number Sense Focus

• Estimation

Mathematical Background

• •

Benchmarks are helpful for making initial estimates. Deciding whether a group of objects is more or less than half of a larger group can make an estimate better. Pictorial representations of quantities give children opportunities to use more than one step in making an estimate.

Using the Activities

• •

In these activities, children estimate how many dots in a collection are white. They are challenged to do this not by counting but by visually surveying the collection.

1. In Activity 1, explain that you will show a picture of 10 dots for a few seconds. Show the first picture, then say:

   • Were more than half of the dots white? If you think the number of white dots was more than 5, give me a thumbs up!

   • Was the number of white dots less than 5? If so, give me a thumbs down!

   • Is it too hard to tell? Hold your thumb sideways!

   Encourage the children to estimate the number of white dots by "eyeballing" the collection rather than counting. If they want to confirm an estimate by counting, fine; but avoid making it a requirement. Focus attention on the number of dots, rather than the area they cover.

2. After each show of thumbs, ask the children to share how they decided. For example, "I thought there more white dots than black dots, so I put my thumb up." Focus the class's attention by showing only one picture at a time.

3. In Activities 2 and 3, explain that every picture contains 20 dots. Uncover each picture one at a time, then ask for a show of thumbs about whether more than half, less than half, or equal numbers of the dots were white (or black). Encourage the children to estimate the number of white (or black) dots in each picture.

Extending the Activities

- Tell the children the number of black dots in each picture, and have them mentally compute the number of white dots.

- Show collections of small objects of three or more colors, and invite estimates of the number of objects of each color in the collection.

- Give groups of children packets of candy-coated chocolates, and have them investigate the number of each color in the packet.

Thumbs Up or Down?

1.
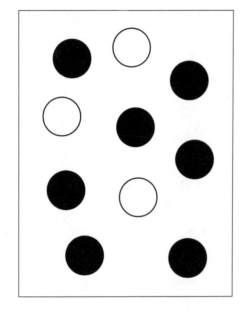

2.
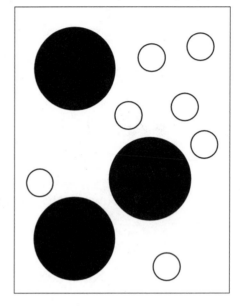

3.
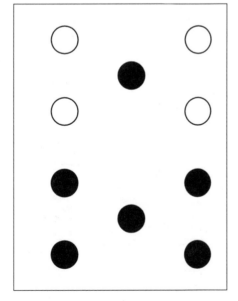

4.
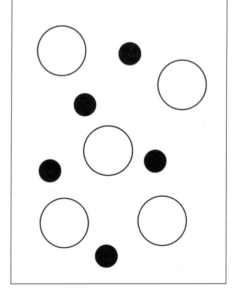

Thumbs Up or Down?

1.

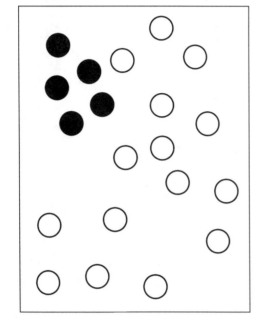

2.

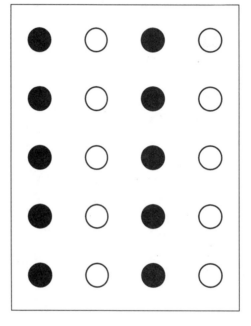

3.

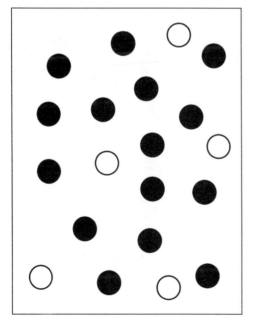

4.

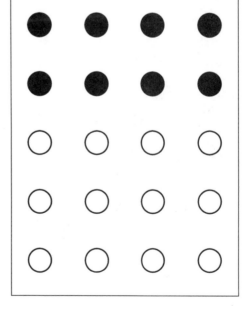

Thumbs Up or Down?

1.

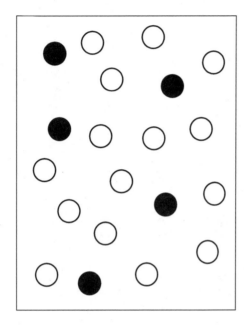

2.

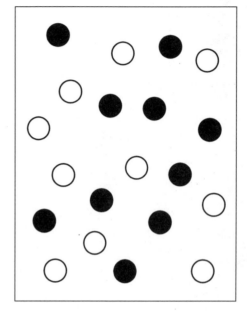

3.

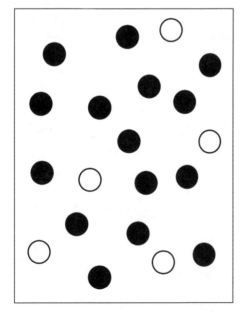

4.

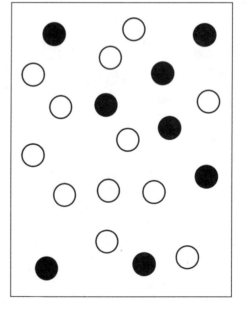

- -

About How Many Do You See?

Number Sense Focus

- Estimation
- Relative size

Mathematical Background

- -

Benchmarks are powerful mathematical tools. If you look at a class of students and think that about 30 are in the class, 30 can serve as a benchmark for estimating the number of students in several classes or in the school. Children need opportunities to learn to use such benchmarks. They must also develop a tolerance for error and learn to recognize when an exact answer may be difficult or impossible to find.

Using the Activities

- -

In these activities, children are encouraged to work with numbers mentally as they use one group of objects as a benchmark for estimating the number of objects in other groups. The value of these activities is the children's sharing of how they made their estimates.

1. Show the top half of Activity 1 for about 20 seconds. Tell the children that there are 20 pennies shown. Continue showing the 20 pennies as you uncover the picture in part 1. After a few more seconds, cover both pictures and ask: Were there more than, less than, or about 20 pennies in the new picture? Show me what you think by giving me a thumbs up, a thumbs down, or a thumb sideways.

2. After the show of thumbs, ask: How many pennies do you think were in the picture? Help the children understand that you want an estimate, not an exact answer. Encourage and accept all estimates. Make a list of the children's estimates, and ask how they made them. Then show the picture again, and have the class count the pennies. Repeat the procedure with the remaining pictures.

3. In Activity 2, the number of buttons in each part matches the number of coins shown in Activity 1, but the buttons are of different sizes.

4. In Activity 3, children compare groups of marbles (parts 1–4 contain 72, 48, 96, and 27 marbles, respectively) to a set of 50 marbles.

   Since the group of 48 marbles is close to the benchmark, students can show thumbs sideways. It is difficult to judge whether values near a benchmark are over or under.

Extending the Activities

• •

- Show the children a pile of 10 to 30 buttons or pennies, and ask them to estimate how many they see.

- Have children estimate the number of pages in a book.

- Talk with the children about other collections of objects they might use as benchmarks for estimating numbers of objects in other groups.

About How Many Do You See?

Here are 20 pennies.

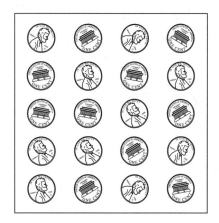

1.

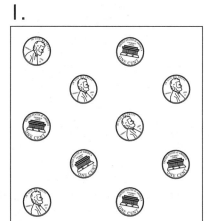

2.

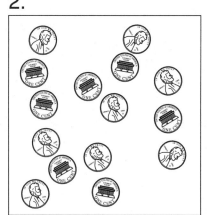

3.

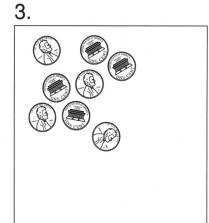

4.

5.

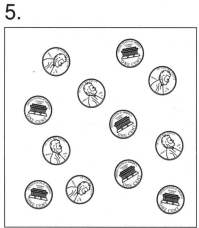

6.

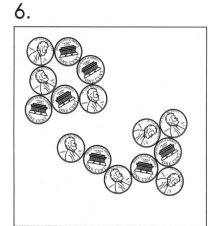

About How Many Do You See?

Here are 20 buttons.

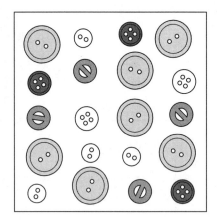

1.

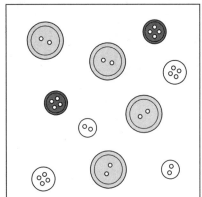

2.

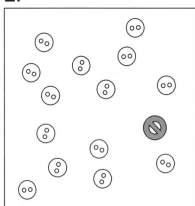

3.

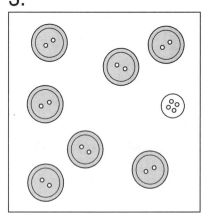

4.

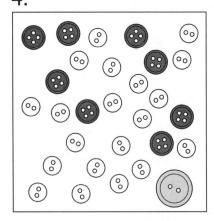

5.

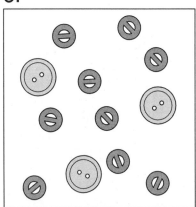

6.

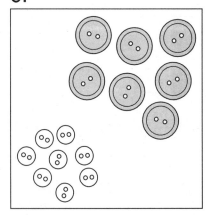

Number SENSE / Grades 1–2

About How Many Do You See?

Here are 50 marbles.

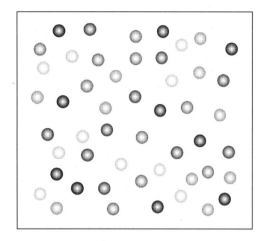

1.

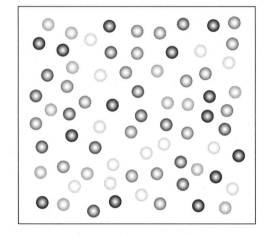

2.

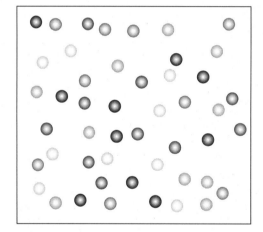

3.

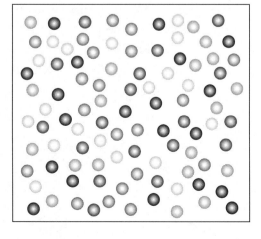

4.

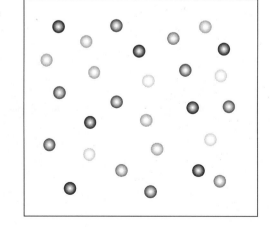

EXPERIENCE 4

Are There More?

Number Sense Focus

- Estimation
- Relative size

Mathematical Background

People with good number sense often have an intuitive sense of how many items are in a collection of objects. Children need to develop a range of strategies for estimating the number of objects in a collection, including reference to a benchmark and the recognition of patterns in the collection.

Using the Activities

In these activities, children indicate whether they think the number of bears in a collection is greater (or smaller) than a given number.

1. In Activity 1, explain that you will show the children a picture of a group of bears. Show the first picture for a few seconds, then ask: Was the number of bears you saw more than 5? more than 10? more than 15? more than 20? Ask for a show of hands after each question. You may want to give the children counters or cubes to help them estimate how many bears they saw. When no more children raise their hands in response to your questions, talk to them about how they made their estimates. Then, help the class count the bears.

2. Use Activity 2 in the same way.

3. In Activity 3, ask the questions in reverse: Are there fewer than 20 bears? fewer than 15? fewer than 10? fewer than 5?

Extending the Activities

- Have children work in pairs, showing a collection of objects for a few seconds and then asking their partner to estimate the number of objects seen.

Are There More?

1.

2.

3.

4.

Are There More?

1.

2.

3.

4.

Are There More?

1.

2.

3.

4.

Number SENSE / Grades 1–2

About How Many Will Fit?

Number Sense Focus

- Estimation
- Relative size

Mathematical Background

Part of good number sense is the ability to compare the relative sizes of objects and to quantify the relationships that are observed.

Using the Activities

In these activities, children are shown a shape and an object and are asked to estimate how many of the objects will fit inside the shape.

1. To prepare for the activities, you will need to collect enough identical objects to fill the three shapes. Choose any of these objects (or any other convenient items): base 10 longs; base 10 units; any type of small cubes, square tiles, counters, pattern blocks (one shape at a time), or coins (one type at a time); thumbtacks, paper clips, dried beans, dried macaroni.

2. In Activity 1, begin with an object of which about 10 to 20 will fit in the square. Show one object next to the square, and ask the children to estimate how many will fit in the square without going over its edges. Ask them to share their thinking, and record the range of estimates they offer.

3. Begin filling the square with the objects (or have a child do it). When the square is about half full, ask whether the children want to change their estimates.

4. When as many objects as possible are in the square, count the total and compare it with the estimates. Talk about the estimates that are reasonable—perhaps within 20% of the total.

5. Choose an object of a different size, and repeat the activity. When a larger object is chosen, check to see whether the children realize that fewer of them will be needed to fill the shape.

6. Use Activities 2 and 3 in the same way, varying the shape and size of the objects.

Extending the Activities

- Have children estimate the number of books that will fit on their desks.

- Place a large sheet of newspaper on the floor, and ask the children to estimate how many of them could stand on it together. Let them test their estimates. Then, ask how much string would be needed to make a loop inside which 10 of the children could stand.

- Show a cardboard box, and ask the children how many cubes, books, or other objects would fit into the box. If possible, let them test their estimates.

About How Many Will Fit?

About How Many Will Fit?

About How Many Will Fit?

EXPERIENCE 6

• •

How Many Pattern Blocks?

Number Sense Focus

- Estimation
- Relative size

Mathematical Background

• •

By comparing the area of a given unit to the area of a larger shape, children strengthen their estimation skills and learn comparison strategies. They also build their ability to reason proportionally (if 10 blue rhombuses fit inside an area, then 20 green triangles would fit).

Using the Activities

• •

In these activities, children estimate how many of a specific pattern block will fit inside a shape.

1. You will need a set of overhead pattern blocks. In Activity 1, show the first shape together with one hexagon. Ask the children: About how many of these hexagons could fit inside the shape? Invite them to offer estimates and to describe their strategies.

2. Fill the shape with hexagons (or invite one of the children to do so). Discuss why their estimates may have been too large or too small.

3. Now show a trapezoid next to the shape, and repeat the activity. Check that children recognize that more trapezoids than hexagons will be needed. Try the rhombus next, and then the triangle. When appropriate, ask such questions as: Do you think it will be more than 10? more than 20? Why do you think that? If the children are still interested, repeat with the other pattern block shapes.

4. Use Activities 2 and 3 in the same way.

Solutions

Activity 1

1. 3 hexagons, 6 trapezoids, 9 rhombuses, 18 triangles
2. 4 hexagons, 8 trapezoids, 12 rhombuses, 24 triangles

Activity 2

5 hexagons, 10 trapezoids, 15 rhombuses, 30 triangles

Activity 3

7 hexagons, 14 trapezoids, 21 rhombuses, 42 triangles

Extending the Activities

• •

- Invite children to work in pairs, drawing around pattern blocks to make shapes for each other to estimate the number of blocks needed to cover them.

How Many Pattern Blocks?

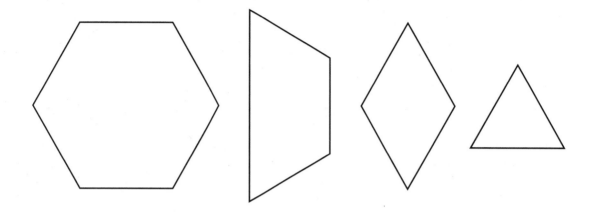

How many will fit?

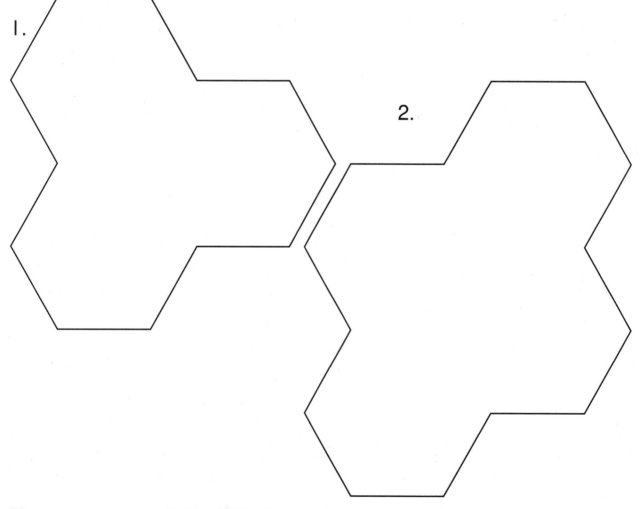

1.

2.

Number SENSE / Grades 1–2

How Many Pattern Blocks?

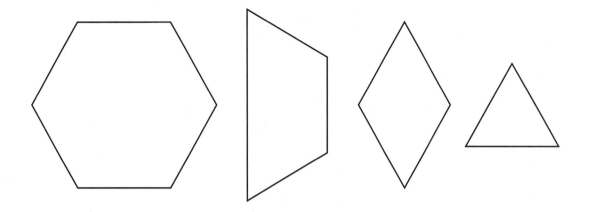

How many will fit?

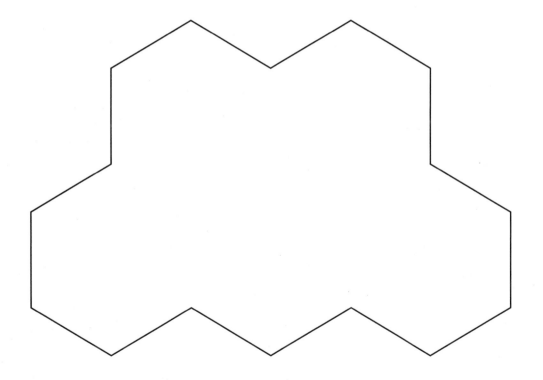

How Many Pattern Blocks?

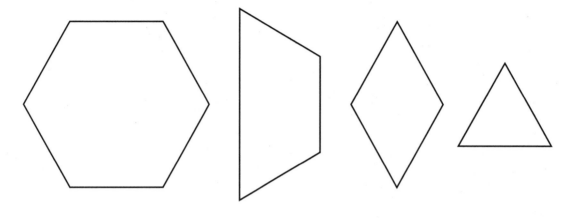

How many will fit?

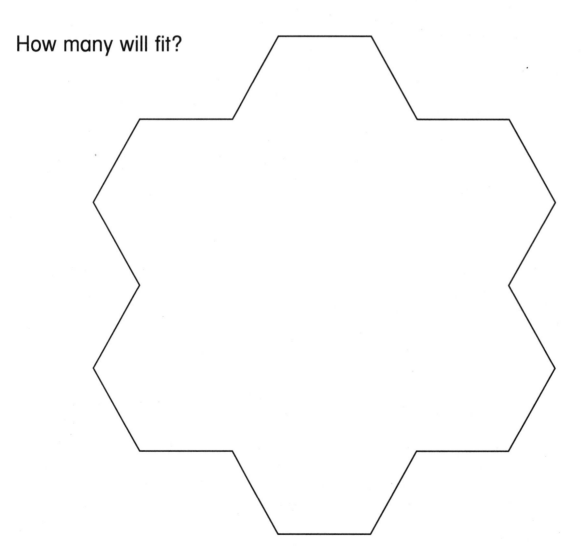

Exploring Measurement

Measurement is the context in which adults use numbers most frequently and in which children and adults best learn to make sense of numbers. Among other things, measurement encompasses length, area, volume, weight, time, and value (such as money). Understanding of the process of measurement and the differing forms and uses of measurement grows in concert with a familiarity with and power over the concept of number.

One's knowledge about measurement begins early and develops over a lifetime. The learning process involves direct measurement using standard tools.

Personal benchmarks allow and promote meaningful comparisons and useful referents, and they help young children develop a sense of numbers and measures. For example:

- "I am 7 years old, and Jean is 8."

- "Jean is taller than I am."

- "My dog is bigger than your dog."

- "Your shoe size is larger than mine."

- "My dad is heavier than my mom."

- "This room is much bigger than my bedroom."

- "My beach ball is larger than that baseball, but it feels lighter."

The variety of measurement activities in this section will encourage children to think about numbers and the process of measurement in creative ways. They promote the recognition that all measurement—except the counting of discrete quantities—is *approximate*. Learning to accept that measurements may be close but not exact is the building of a tolerance for error. Such tolerance develops slowly, and children need many experiences with measurement approximation to become comfortable with the concept of error.

Time Out

Number Sense Focus

- Measurement
- Relative size
- Multiple representation
- Reasonableness

Mathematical Background

Concepts involving units of time—seconds, minutes, hours, days, weeks, months, years—develop slowly. Children learn the relationships among these units as they make personal connections to them.

Using the Activities

These activities help children to establish meaningful relationships among several units of time. In the process, they develop their vocabulary and apply it to real-life situations.

1. Children often measure time using personal benchmarks, such as their grade, their birthday, and special or disturbing events. As a warm-up, ask the children to share three things that happened

    - before they came to school today

    - after they came to school today

    As children offer their ideas, ask how they decided in which category each event belonged.

2. Activity 1 asks children to place personal events into different time frames. As you make each list, encourage the children to share how they know an event belongs in a particular time category.

3. Activity 2 focuses on the second and the minute as units of time. Again, ask the children to tell how they know an item belongs in a particular list.

4. Activity 3 uses a child's birth year as a benchmark. First, ask the children to share their birth years. Then, encourage them to describe something they know happened before their birth and something they know happened after their birth, and to tell how they know when each event happened.

Extending the Activities

• •

- Help children figure out when they were 100 days old.

- Ask children in what year they will be 10 years old.

- Ask children to name something that happened last month (year) and this month (year).

Time Out

Monday	Tuesday	Wednesday	Thursday	Friday	Saturday	Sunday

Name 3 things that happened:

Today   Yesterday

This week   Last week

Name 3 things that will happen:

Tomorrow   Next week

Time Out

Things I can do in one second:

Things I can't do in one second:

Things I can do in one minute:

Things I can't do in one minute:

Time Out

Things that happened before I was born:

Things that happened after I was born:

EXPERIENCE 8

How Long Is a Handful?

Number Sense Focus

- Measurement
- Estimation

Mathematical Background

Children enjoy and learn a great deal from experimenting with units of measurement. Their experiences should include a range of units, both standard and nonstandard, and they should have opportunities to make guesses and estimates and then measure to test their estimates.

Using the Activities

1. As a warm-up, prepare a large dish of assorted buttons (or other items that come in more than one size, such as coins or counters). Ask the children to think about two questions:

   - About how many buttons can one person pick up in one hand?

   - About how far will those buttons reach if they are laid end to end?

   Write the various estimates for each question on the board.

2. Invite several children, one at a time, to take a handful of buttons from the dish, then count them and lay them end to end. Help them to measure the length of each line of buttons.

3. Make a table of the results, including the number of buttons in each handful and how far the buttons stretched. Ask the children: Do the greatest number of buttons necessarily stretch the farthest? (*Not necessarily; it depends on the size of the buttons.*)

4. Activities 1 and 2 extend the work done with the real objects and promote discussion about measuring with nonstandard units. Encourage the children to explain their answers to each question.

Extending the Activities

- Given the results of the experiment, have children predict how far 100 buttons would stretch, or how many buttons it would take to go across the teacher's desk.

- Have the class explore which child can pick up the most buttons in one hand.

- Challenge children to find out whether they can pick up more buttons with their left hand or their right hand.

How Long Is a Handful?

Here are the buttons four children picked up with one hand.

Kai

Kelly

Shamaria

Al

Who do you think has the biggest hand? Why?

How Long Is a Handful?

Here is how four children used buttons to measure the width of a book.

How many buttons did each child use?

Who do you think made the best measurement?

EXPERIENCE 9

Human Balance

Number Sense Focus

- Measurement
- Estimation

Mathematical Background

Adults often use personal benchmarks to judge the weight of objects. Such benchmarks evolve from experience. For example, chefs may use their familiarity with 5-pound bags of sugar; people who lifts weight may find 10, 20, and 40 pounds useful benchmarks.

Using the Activities

In this experience, children are introduced to the concept of benchmarks. They mentally and physically use benchmarks to judge relative weight.

1. To prepare, collect several everyday objects (such as books, canned good, a loaded backpack) weighing between $\frac{1}{2}$ pound and 5 pounds, four or five 1-pound boxes of sugar (to use as benchmark weights), and a small scale. Put the objects you have collected on a table.

2. Ask the children to *think about* and *imagine* how heavy the objects are. Ask: Suppose you picked up two of these objects, one in each hand, and held your arms out to the sides. Which object would feel heavier?

3. Let several children choose pairs of objects, estimate which is heavier, then be a "human balance" to test their estimate. Ask questions, such as:

   - Is the biggest thing always the heaviest?

   - Is the smallest thing always the lightest?

4. Put a box of sugar on the scale and show the children that it weighs approximately 1 pound (point out that the box label also indicates this weight). Let the children use the box of sugar as a benchmark to judge the weight of other objects by holding the box of sugar in one hand and another object in the other hand. Ask:

   • Which objects do you think weigh less than 1 pound?

   • Which objects do you think weigh more than 1 pound?

5. Finally, give them the task of estimating the weight of each item on the table by assigning it a numerical value. Encourage them to think about each item in terms of the box of sugar. Is it the same as a half a box of sugar ($\frac{1}{2}$ pound)? two boxes of sugar (2 pounds)? five boxes of sugar (5 pounds)?

6. After the work with the real objects, show Activity 1. And ask the children to estimate about how many of each object would make about a pound. (You might want to ask about how many of each would make a kilogram; if so, provide the class with objects to use as benchmarks for 1 kilogram.) In Activity 1, children are given several possibilities from which to choose. Ask them to explain their thinking.

7. In Activity 2, the children are to suggest answers on their own.

Solutions

Activity 1 and *Activity 2*

Answers will vary. Accept any reasonable answer if children can explain their thinking.

Extending the Activities

• •

• Ask the children to find a package, can, or box at home tonight that weighs $\frac{1}{2}$ pound (the pantry is a good place to look; their families can help them check package labels). Then, they can use the object to judge the weight of three other items. The next day, let the children share what they found.

• Let the children use 5- and 10-pound sacks of flour or sugar to judge the weight of larger objects, such as their baby brother or sister or their desk.

Human Balance

About how many of each will make a pound?

Oranges	1	5	15

Pencils	8	80	400

Tennis shoes	1 pair	2 pairs	5 pairs

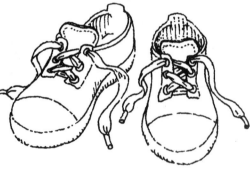

Math books	1	2	3

Computer disks	2	10	20

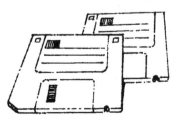

Human Balance

About how many of each will make a pound?

Staplers

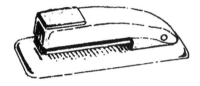

Soccer balls

Jars of paste

School milk cartons

Balloons

EXPERIENCE 10

• •

How Much Does It Hold?

Number Sense Focus

• Measurement
• Estimation

Mathematical Background

• •

Judging the capacity of containers of different sizes and shapes requires a grasp of the concept of conservation of quantity, which develops with experience and maturity. A familiarity with common units—such as a cup, quart, and gallon—is also useful, as they serve as benchmarks for judging the capacity of nonstandard containers.

Using the Activity

• •

In this experience, children judge the relative sizes of containers and use what they know about one container—the benchmark—to judge the capacity of other containers.

1. To prepare, collect five to eight bottles and jars of varying shapes and sizes, ranging from 2 cups to 1 gallon, including one with a capacity of 1 quart. Remove any labels, and add an identifying letter (A, B, C, . . .) to each. You will also need a 1-cup measuring cup and access to water.

2. Arrange the containers on a table so the class can see them. Ask: Which bottle do you think holds the most water? the least water?

3. Explain that one of the containers holds 1 quart of liquid. Ask the children to think about which container it might be. Ask other questions, such as:

    • How much is a quart?

    • What kinds of things come in a quart-size container?

- How can we identify which bottle holds 1 quart?

- Suppose we use a measuring cup to fill the bottle you've chosen. How many cups do you think will fill the bottle?

Ask children to write down their ideas. Begin filling the bottle. After each cup is poured, ask whether the children want to change their estimates. Continue pouring until the bottle is full, and then confirm the number of cups in a quart.

4. Once the quart bottle is identified, ask the children to name the containers they think will hold more than a quart of water and those that will hold less than a quart of water. Arrange the containers into two groups according to their predictions. Let the children test their predictions by pouring water from the quart container into the other containers.

5. Choose a bottle, and ask the children to use the quart bottle as a benchmark for estimating how many cups the chosen bottle will hold and then to check their prediction by pouring.

6. Use Activity 1 as a follow-up to the work with the real containers. If the children are unfamiliar with any of the items that are pictured, make real containers available. Show each picture, and help the children identify each container. Then, ask these questions:

- Which containers hold about a quart?

- Which containers hold more than a quart?

- Which containers hold less than a quart?

- Which container holds the most?

- Which containers are you unsure about?

Help the children put the objects in order by capacity.

Extending the Activity

• •

- Allow groups of children to estimate the order of a group of containers by capacity. They can record their estimated order, then experiment by filling the containers with water or sand and making comparisons.

How Much Does It Hold?

Which holds more than a quart? less than a quart? about a quart?

Which holds more than a quart? less than a quart? about a quart?

Numbers on a Line

Number Sense Focus

- Measurement
- Estimation

Mathematical Background

The number line is a valuable model for representing the size and order of numbers. Children will become more comfortable with the number line as they use it.

Using the Activity

1. For this activity, you will need an 8-foot length of string, 10 to 15 clothespins, and a set of index cards numbered from 0 to 30. Stretch the string across the room like a clothesline, perhaps along the chalkboard. Place the 0 and 30 cards at the ends of the line using clothespins, and distribute the other cards to the children.

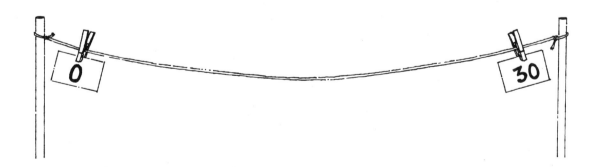

2. Point to the center of the string (halfway between 0 and 30) and ask a child to name the number this point represents. Have the child holding 15 hang the card on the line. Point slightly to the left of 15, and ask what number might go there. Several answers may be suggested (such as 12, 13, or 14). Accept whatever suggestion children feel most comfortable with, and remind them that they can adjust the positions of the cards later. Ask other children to hang their numbers as the class helps locate the positions, focusing on *reasonable* rather than *exact* locations. Encourage children to explain their thinking, emphasizing the use of terms such as *between, more than,* and *less than.*

3. Follow this with Activities 1 and 2. If necessary, use the clothesline model to help the children find the values of the blank cards.

4. The last number line in Activity 2 shows only a single value of 10, so the values of the other cards depend on the scale. The line could go from 0 to 20, from 5 to 15, or some other range. Encourage children to explain their answers; accept any values satisfying the conditions.

Extending the Activity

• •

- Repeat the activity (using either the physical model or a sketch) with other endpoints, such as 5 and 15 or 0 and 40. Ask the children: What numbers can be placed on this number line? Where will they go?

- Make new number cards (for example, from 30 to 60) and repeat the clothesline activity.

Numbers on a Line

What number belongs on each blank card? Tell why.

1.

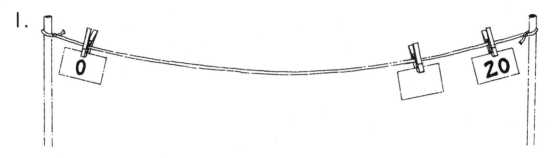

2.

3.

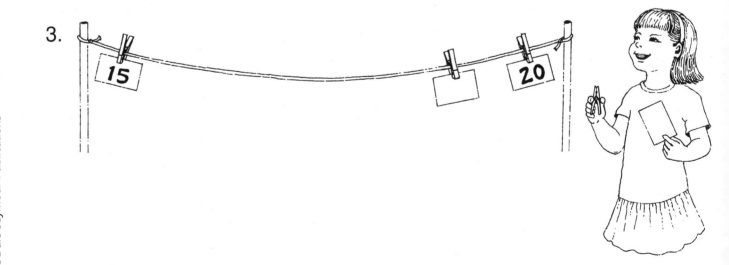

Numbers on a Line

What number belongs on each blank card? Tell why.

1.

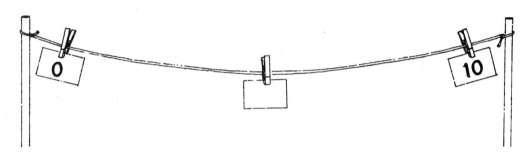

2.

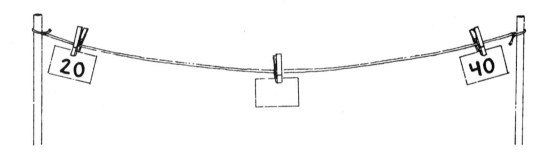

3.

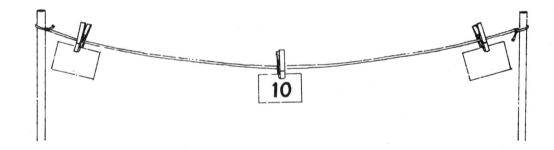

Number SENSE / Grades 1–2

Exploring Mental Computation

Being able to calculate mentally, without the use of external memory aids (including paper and pencil), is a valuable skill. The illustrations show that doing computations mentally is often easier and quicker than performing written algorithms. One benefit of mental computation is that it can lead to a better understanding of place value, mathematical operations, and basic number properties. The stickers example $(2 \times 4¢ = 2 \times 5¢ - 2 \times 1¢)$ demonstrates mental application of the distributive property and involves operations and basic number properties.

Research shows that children tend to rely on written computational algorithms and do not consider mental computation a viable option—perhaps because they have learned that in school, everything must be written. Children need encouragement to develop mental-computation skills and to apply them whenever they are appropriate.

Mental computation lends itself to a variety of thinking strategies. For example, consider these three approaches to calculating 15 + 9:

- 15 + 9 can be calculated by adding 15 and 10 then subtracting 1 to get 24.

- 5 + 9 is 14, and 10 more is 24.

- 15 + 5 is 20, and 4 more is 24.

As children learn to manipulate numbers in their heads, they develop better number sense and increased confidence in their mathematical abilities. This confidence will encourage them to consider mental computation as an option when straightforward calculations are encountered. Regular opportunities to develop, discuss, and apply mental computation strategies not only contribute to number sense, but can significantly improve a child's ability to think about numbers in a variety of ways.

Will You Do It in Your Head?

Number Sense Focus

- Mental computation
- Number relationships

Mathematical Background

Children need to learn to make sensible decisions about how to perform calculations—mentally, using a formal or informal written algorithm, or with a calculator. How the numbers in a computation are related to each other and the operations involved influence whether the computation can be determined mentally. For example, young children can usually determine $16 + 7$ mentally, but they find 16×7 very difficult. Children's reliance on written computation seems to increase in the middle grades and probably reflects the emphasis given to it in school. Calculators are powerful tools, but wise use of them should be encouraged. Mental computation should always be the first option considered.

Using the Activities

These activities encourage children to think about and do addition and subtraction computations mentally and to talk about their strategies.

1. In each activity, show the illustration at the top. Ask children for other ways to do the computation, and talk about their ideas. Ask which method of doing the calculation they prefer: mentally, with pencil and paper, or with a calculator? Encourage them to explain their choice; this sharing is the heart of these activities.

2. Reveal the computations one at a time, and ask children how they would prefer to do each one. Focus on the idea that both the numbers

and the operation determine how easy or difficult it would be to do the computation mentally. For example, 23 + 7 is easier to do mentally than 23 – 7, and 38 – 8 is easier than 38 + 8. These issues are personal, so there are no correct answers; what is important is that children think about these computations, decide what is easy or hard for them, and explain their thinking.

3. Make a list of the "easy" problems offered, which will help children realize that what is easy for them may not be easy for everyone. Encourage children to explain why they find a particular computation easy.

Extending the Activities

• •

- Ask children to pick a computation that they chose to do mentally and to tell how they did it.

- Ask children to make up a new computation that is easy to do mentally and to tell why it is easy.

- Ask for a computation that is hard to do mentally, and ask children why it is hard.

Will You Do It in Your Head?

8 + 2 = 10,
plus 5 is 15.

8 + 7

Which are easy to do in your head? Why?

1. 9 + 2

2. 80 + 70

3. 8 + 13

4. 80 + 10

5. 18 + 6

6. 18 + 26

7. 10 + 10 + 10

8. 2 + 2 + 2 + 2 + 2 + 2

9. 25 + 25

10. 38 + 66

Will You Do It in Your Head?

Which are easy to do in your head? Why?

1. $15 - 5$

2. $150 - 70$

3. $35 - 17$

4. $50 - 7$

5. $100 - 50$

6. $126 - 10$

7. $43 - 10$

8. $62 - 25$

9. $19 - 6$

10. $138 - 136$

Will You Do It in Your Head?

Which are easy to do in your head? Why?

1. 2 + 4 + 8

2. 1 + 2 + 3 + 4 + 5

3. 11 + 12 + 13 + 14 + 15

4. 8 + 9 − 6

5. 27 + 16 − 16

6. 8 − 7 + 6 − 5 + 4

7. 243 − 87 + 85

8. 20 + 20 + 20 + 20 + 20

9. 3 + 168

10. 9 + 16 − 9

Will You Do It in Your Head?

Which are easy to do in your head? Why?

1. 1 + 9

2. 20 + 20 + 20 + 20

3. 21 + 19

4. 25 + 26

5. 450 + 100

6. 750 + 75

7. 3 + 3 + 3 + 3 + 3

8. 50 + 7 + 50

9. 51 + 51 + 51 + 51

10. 19 + 20 + 21

Will You Do It in Your Head?

Which are easy to do in your head? Why?

1. 80 + 20 + 90

2. 700 + 50 + 6

3. 60 + 80 + 40 + 10

4. 50 + 400 + 10

5. 75 + 50 + 25

6. 10 + 20 + 30

7. 99 + 99

8. 9 + 10 + 11

9. 24 + 25 + 26

10. 50 + 50 + 50 + 50 + 50 + 50 + 50

EXPERIENCE 13

Today's Target

Number Sense Focus

- Mental computation
- Number relationships
- Multiple representation

Mathematical Background

We frequently use relationships between numbers to simplify mental calculations. To compute $7 + 8$, for example, we could use the relationship $8 = 3 + 5$ and calculate $7 + 3 + 5$. The ability to quickly see the relationships among numbers helps us to choose calculation strategies.

Using the Activities

In these activities, children are presented with a target number and are invited to create calculations for which the target number is the answer.

1. In each activity, show the target number. Ask for some calculations that would produce the number.

2. Reveal and explain each restriction in turn, and ask for calculations of this type that will produce the target number. You may want to make counters available for children to use to model possible solutions.

3. Use Activity 4 with a target number of your choice.

Extending the Activities

- Invite children to challenge the class with a restriction of their own for a given target number.

- Create other restrictions and other target numbers, such as the date or the day of the year.

- Challenge the class to work individually to write as many calculations as possible in a given amount of time (say, 2 minutes) that produce the target number. To encourage creativity, make a rule that a calculation will score only if no one else in class has thought of it.

Today's Target

Today's target is **5**

Try to make the target by

1. adding two numbers.

2. subtracting two numbers.

3. adding three numbers.

4. adding and subtracting.

5. starting with a number greater than 10.

6. starting with 5.

7. using the easiest way.

8. using the hardest way.

Today's Target

Today's target is **8**

Try to make the target by

1. adding two different numbers.

2. subtracting two numbers.

3. adding three numbers.

4. adding and subtracting.

5. starting with a number greater than 10.

6. adding numbers that are the same.

7. using the easiest way.

8. using the hardest way.

Today's Target

Today's target is **10**

Try to make the target by

1. adding two numbers.

2. subtracting two numbers.

3. adding three numbers.

4. adding and subtracting.

5. starting with a number greater than 20.

6. starting with 10.

7. using the easiest way.

8. using the hardest way.

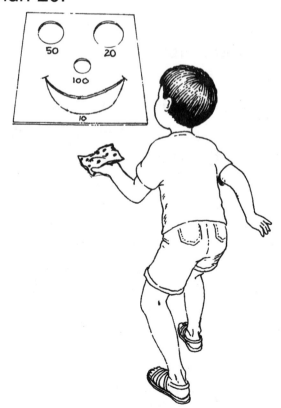

Today's Target

Today's target is ☐

Try to make the target by

1. adding two different numbers.

2. Subtracting two numbers.

3. adding three numbers.

4. adding and subtracting.

5. starting with a number greater than 10.

6. adding numbers that are the same.

7. using the easiest way.

8. using the hardest way.

EXPERIENCE 14

Adding Compatibles

Number Sense Focus

- Mental computation
- Multiple representation
- Number relationships

Mathematical Background

Numbers that are easy to compute mentally and seem to go together naturally—such as numbers totaling a multiple of 10—are called *compatible numbers*. Compatible numbers help simplify mental computations. To add $4 + 3 + 8 + 7 + 6$, we may reason that $4 + 6 = 10$, and $3 + 7 = 10$, and $20 + 8 = 28$.

Using the Activities

In these activities, children focus on pairs of numbers that make 10. For one or more of these activities, you may wish to make copies for children to work on individually either instead of using the transparency or for consolidation after you have used the transparency with the class.

1. In Activity 1, explain to children that they will see part of a drawing of two hands. They are to decide how many fingers they see and how many are missing—that is, how many more fingers are needed to make 10. Show each drawing for a few seconds. Encourage children to describe how they decided on the number of fingers shown and the number missing. For example:

   - "I see 5 on one hand and 3 on the other. That makes 8."

   - "There are 2 fingers missing, so there are 8 showing."

2. In Activity 2, strings of between 1 and 10 beads are shown. Show the first string of beads, and verify that the children know that 10 beads are in the string. Show each string for a few seconds, and ask children how many beads they saw and how many were missing—that is, how many more are needed to make 10. Encourage them to share how they thought about each problem.

3. In Activity 3, ask children to identify pairs of numbers that add to 10. Mark the pairs or cover them with counters until only one digit (5) remains.

Extending the Activities

• Have children work on the activities on their own.

• Have children work in pairs. One holds up some fingers, and the other says how many are held up and how many are concealed.

• Have children thread beads, changing color after every five beads. Each child can ask a partner to estimate, and then calculate, how many beads there are in the chain.

• Have children create sets of numbers like those in Activity 3, with pairs of numbers totaling 10 for a partner to discover.

Adding Compatibles

How many fingers do you see?

How many more will make 10?

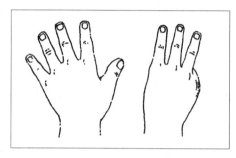 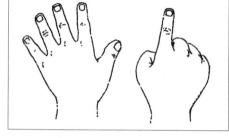

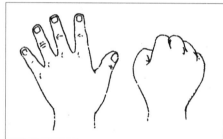 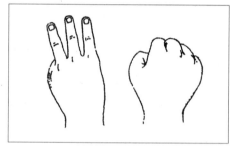

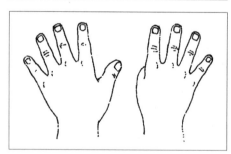 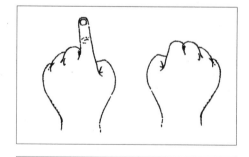

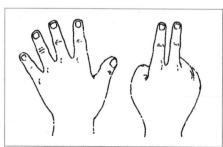 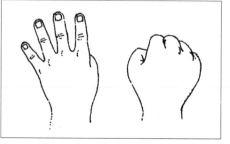

Number SENSE / Grades 1–2

Adding Compatibles

How many beads do you see?

How many more will make 10?

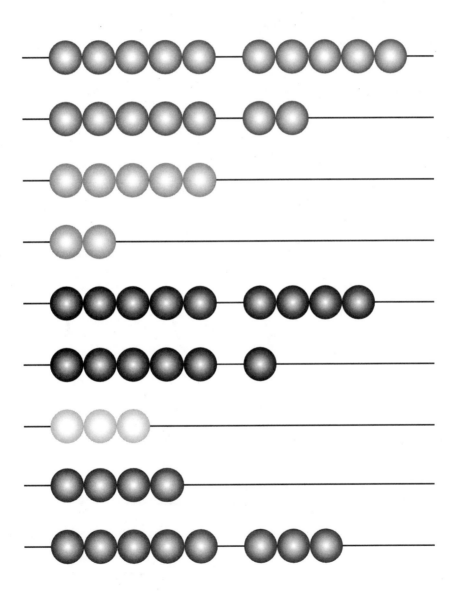

Adding Compatibles

Cover pairs of numbers that add to 10.

Which number is left over?

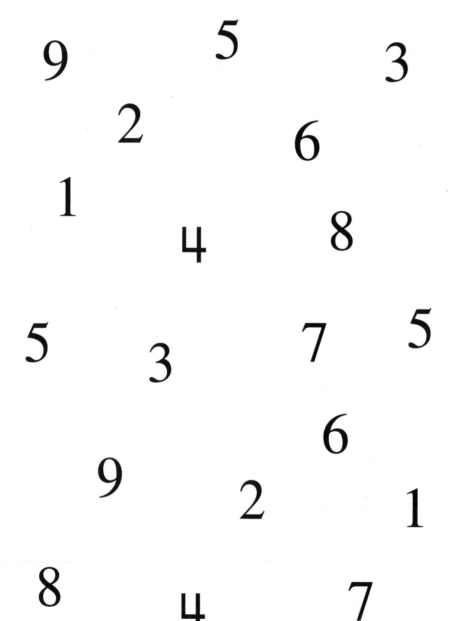

How Many Dots?

Number Sense Focus

• Mental computation

Mathematical Background

Seeing spatial relationships, recognizing and analyzing patterns, and using relationships and patterns to count and quantify are valuable number sense skills.

Using the Activities

In these activities, children are shown arrays of dots for a short time. To mentally calculate how many dots are in each group, the children must often rely on arranging the dots they saw into recognizable patterns.

1. In Activities 1 and 2, the dots are in a grid of 10 squares. Some of the dots form a pattern, within which may be subpatterns. Show the first set of dots for several seconds. Cover the image, and invite the children to say how many dots they think they saw. Emphasize that they aren't estimating the number but finding a way to mentally calculate it. It may be helpful for them to work in pairs and share strategies. Show the image again if necessary. You may need to establish that a filled frame holds 10 dots.

2. Ask individuals or pairs to share their answers and strategies. For example, for part 2, children may say:

    • "I saw 4 rows of 2, which makes 8 in all."

    • "I saw 2 columns of 4 dots, so that's 8."

    • "I saw 2 blank squares, and 10 – 2 = 8."

3. Use the remaining sets of dots in the same way. In Activity 3, the dots are in a grid of 20 squares. Ask the children why some sets of dots are more difficult to count. *(Because the dots don't form a pattern.)*

Extending the Activities

• •

- Have children make similar puzzles to try out on each other.

How Many Dots?

How many dots do you see? How did you count them?

1.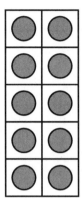

2.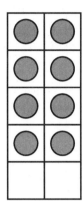

3.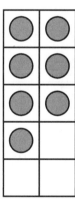

4.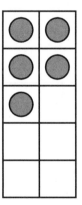

5.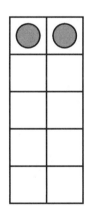

6.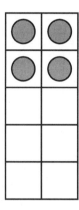

7.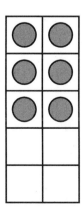

8.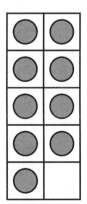

9.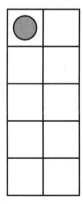

How Many Dots?

How many dots do you see? How did you count them?

1.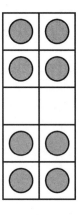

2.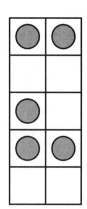

3.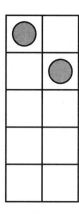

4.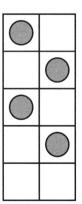

5.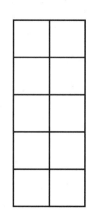

6.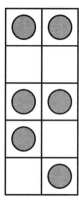

7.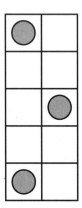

8.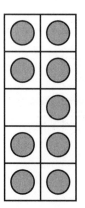

9.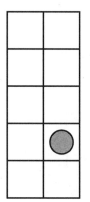

How Many Dots?

How many dots do you see? How did you count them?

1.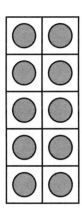

2.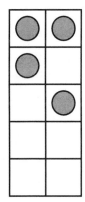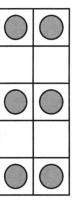

3.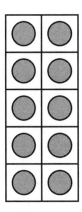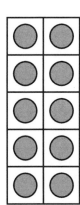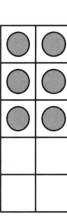

4.

5.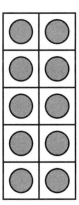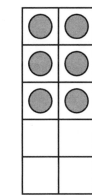

6.

EXPERIENCE 16

· ·

Make It Easier

Number Sense Focus

- Mental computation
- Number relationships

Mathematical Background

· ·

To calculate mentally, we need a secure knowledge of the addition of numbers up to 10 + 10 and their related subtractions. On their way to instant recall of these facts, many children use strategies for working them out mentally, which they discard as they learn the facts. However, some children do not acquire these strategies on their own, instead relying on inefficient counting-by-ones procedures.

Using the Activities

· ·

These activities will help children acquire reliable procedures for computing basic facts. Three particularly helpful strategies are introduced: starting with the largest number, bridging 10, and using doubles.

1. Explain to the children that they will see some ways to make adding and subtracting easier. Show the top part of Activity 1, and explain what is happening: the person is holding $2 in one hand and $9 in the other and wants to add the amounts together. If we start from $2, we must add nine single bills. If we start from $9, we only need to add two bills. Encourage children to explain why it is easier to start with the larger number. Their verbalization will help them to adopt the procedure as their own.

2. Show each example in turn, and have children give their answer and describe how to use the procedure of starting with the largest number.

If they suggest other appropriate methods, discuss them, but make it clear that you wish everyone to practice this method.

3. Activity 2 explores the bridging-10 strategy. Show the top illustration, and ask the children to explain why first making 10 from the numbers, then adding the remaining 3, is an easy way to add the numbers. Then, have them do each calculation by bridging 10. Use the second half to help children use the strategy with subtraction.

4. Activity 3 uses doubles to make addition and subtraction easier.

Extending the Activities

- Have children suggest and work through other examples of calculations that could be done using each of the strategies. Some children may be ready to explore the use of these strategies with larger numbers, such as 97 + 6 and 23 − 5.

Make It Easier

Try these an easy way.

1. 1 + 6   2. 2 + 5

3. 2 + 8   4. 3 + 8

5. 3 + 9   6. 2 + 7

7. 3 + 7   8. 4 + 9

9. 3 + 10   10. 4 + 8

Make It Easier

Try these by bridging 10.

1. 8 + 3

2. 7 + 5

3. 9 + 4

4. 8 + 6

5. 7 + 6

6. 9 + 5

Try these by bridging 10.

7. 12 − 3

8. 11 − 4

9. 13 − 6

10. 14 − 5

11. 13 − 4

12. 13 − 5

Make It Easier

Try these by using doubles.

1. 3 + 4   2. 5 + 7

3. 4 + 5   4. 6 + 8

5. 8 + 9   6. 7 + 9

7. 5 + 4   8. 6 + 5

9. 7 + 5   11. 8 + 7

11. 9 + 8   12. 8 + 6

Skip Counting

Number Sense Focus

• Mental computation

Mathematical Background

We frequently use the multiplication relationships up to 10×10. One step on the way to instant recall of these facts is *skip counting*—that is, counting up from 0 in multiples of a number. Not only does this help with learning the multiplication tables, but it dissuades children from counting by ones.

Using the Activities

Make copies of Activity 1 for the children so they can place their fingers on the chart during the discussion. It is also a nice model with which children can practice.

1. Show Activity 1, and ask children to spread their hands out as shown in the illustration. Ask: Which is the second finger from the left? the fourth? the sixth? the ninth? Continue until they can easily associate each finger with an ordinal number.

2. Have children count from 1 to 10, looking at each finger in turn from the left as they count. Say:

   • Show the finger you look at when you say 4. Show the finger you look at when you say 9.

   • What number do you say on each thumb?

   • What number do you say on your third finger? on your seventh finger?

3. Now repeat the activity, this time counting in 2s (2, 4, 6, . . .), having the children look at each finger in turn as they count aloud. They may benefit by lifting and lowering each finger as they count on it. Point to the row of circled numbers showing multiples of 2, and ask questions such as:

  • On which finger do you say 4? 6? 12? 20?

  • What do you say on your third finger? your fifth finger? your seventh finger?

  Encourage children to look at their fingers or the numerals as they answer until they have the confidence to answer without looking.

4. Activity 2 will give children more practice in relating multiples of 2 to fingers. (At this stage, don't be in a hurry to translate "The number I say on my sixth finger is 12" into the symbolism "$6 \times 2 = 12$." The idea here is to give informal experiences that will make the later transition more natural.)

5. Activities 1 and 2 can be used successively with multiples of each digit from 2 to 10 when the children are ready to skip count in 3s, 4s, or any other number up to 10.

6. Use Activity 3 as a challenge when the children are familiar with multiples of numbers from 2 to 5.

Solutions

Activity 3

1. 3s	2. 4s	3. 2s	4. 4s	5. 2s
6. 3s	7. 5s	8. 4s	9. 5s	10. 3s

Extending the Activities

• •

  • Encourage children to skip count in 2s (or 3s, or whatever multiple is appropriate) as quickly as possible, touching their desks with successive fingers as they say each multiple: "2, 4, 6, 8, . . . , 18, 20."

Skip Counting

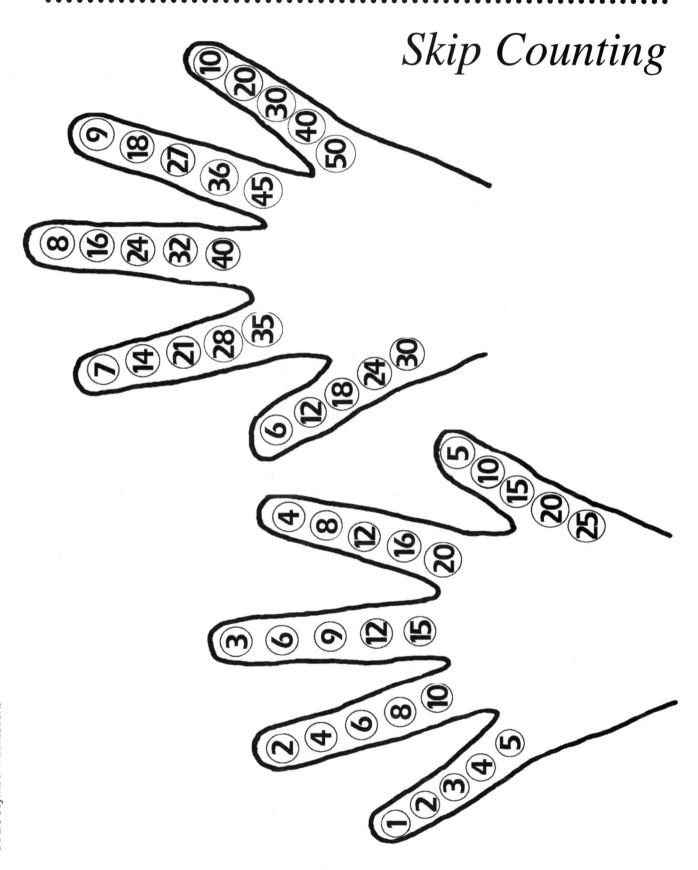

Skip Counting

What number will you say on each finger?

1.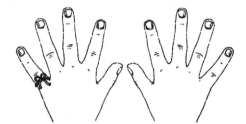

2.

3.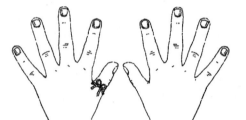

4.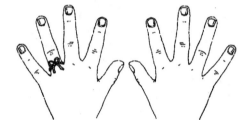

5.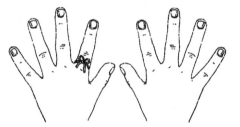

6.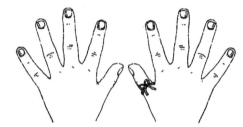

7.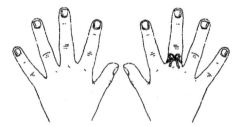

8.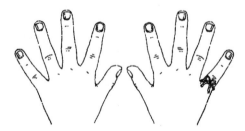

9.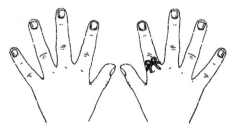

10.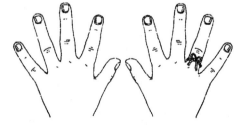

Skip Counting

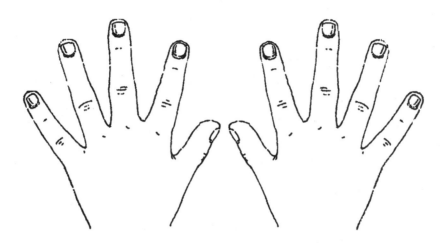

What would you be skip counting by if on your . . .

1. second finger you said 6?

2. third finger you said 12?

3. seventh finger you said 14?

4. fourth finger you said 16?

5. ninth finger you said 18?

6. sixth finger you said 18?

7. ninth finger you said 45?

8. sixth finger you said 24?

9. fifth finger you said 25?

10. eighth finger you said 24?

EXPERIENCE 18

••••••••••••••••••••••••••

Which Path Will You Take?

Number Sense Focus

- Mental computation
- Multiple representation

Mathematical Background

•••••••••••••••••••••••••••••

Mental computation involves thinking about numbers, recognizing numbers that are easy to compute, applying mathematical properties, and exploring relationships. Chaining computations together may involve taking advantage of inverse relationships. For example, we could compute $5 + 10 - 10$ by thinking that $5 + 10 = 15$ and $15 - 10 = 5$. A more efficient solution would take advantage of the fact that $10 - 10 = 0$.

Using the Activities

••••••••••••••••••••••••••••••

In these activities, children practice mental computation in an interesting and challenging context.

1. Make sure the children understand that they begin at the bottom of each maze with the Start Number and travel along the various paths by performing the computations shown. When the rules are clear, help the children work through the questions in Activities 1, 2, and 3.

2. The blank maze in Activity 4 may be used in several ways:

   - Ask children to write in values and operations and compute each person's number.

   - Provide numbers for each person, and have the children enter values and operations to make those numbers.

   - Provide all the numbers, and have the children enter operations that will produce the correct results.

3. Activity 3 involves simple multiplication. Use it with second grade only after you have introduced the notation for multiplication.

Solutions

Activity 1

1. Flora's
2. Dave's
3. 13
4. Ellen's (7)
5. Barb's (15)

Activity 2

1. Cy's
2. Eli's
3. 14
4. Batai's (15)
5. Cy, Art, Drew, Eli, Fu-Sheng, Batai

Activity 3

1. Faye's
2. Don's (7)
3. Faye, Don, Bill, Clay, Ally, Elke
4. Clay's
5. Don's and Faye's

Extending the Activities

• •

- Ask children to change the Start Number and see how the people's numbers change.

- Have children change one operation and find the new results.

Which Path Will You Take?

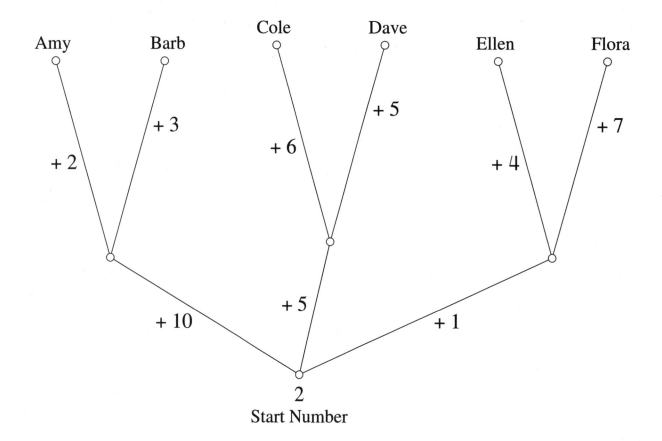

1. Which path gives 10?

2. Which path gives 12?

3. What does Cole's path give?

4. Which path gives the smallest number?

5. Which path gives the greatest number?

Which Path Will You Take?

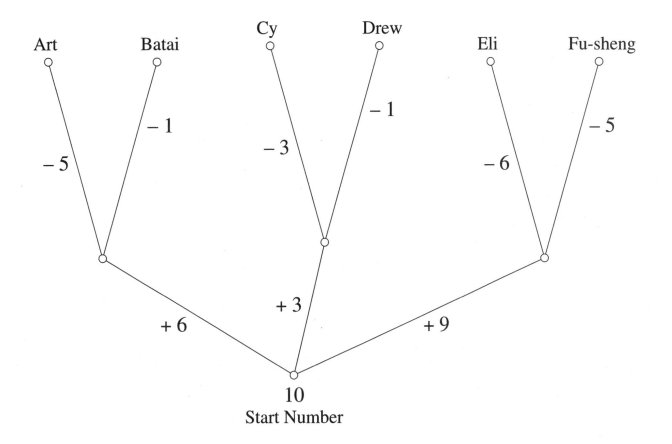

1. Which path gives 10?

2. Which path gives 13?

3. What does Fu-Sheng's path give?

4. Which path gives the greatest number?

5. Arrange the names in order of their numbers.

Which Path Will You Take?

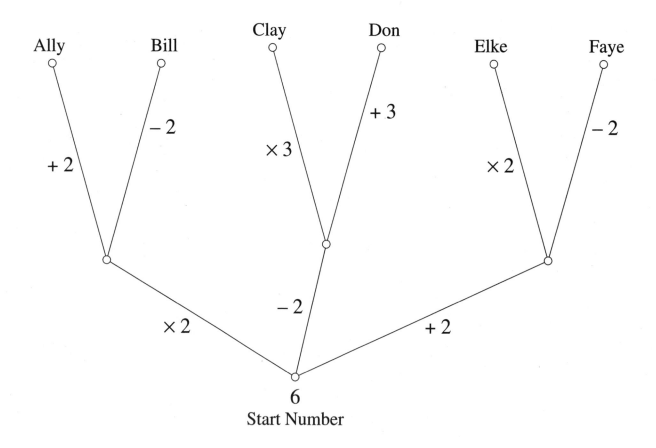

1. Which path gives the Start Number?

2. Which path gives an odd number?

3. Arrange the names in order of their numbers.

4. If the Start Number were 5, Ally's number would be 12 instead of 14, or 2 less. Whose number would be 3 less?

5. If the Start Number were 5, whose number would be 1 less?

Which Path Will You Take?

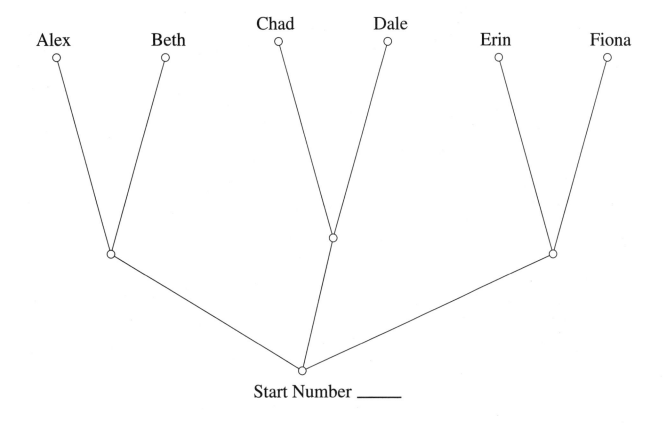

Alex   Beth   Chad   Dale   Erin   Fiona

Start Number _____

EXPERIENCE 19

•••••••••••••••••••••••••••••

What Did I Buy?

Number Sense Focus

- Mental computation
- Number relationships

Mathematical Background

•••••••••••••••••••••••••••••

Mental computation is greatly enhanced by the recognition of compatible numbers—for example, pairs of numbers that total a multiple of 10, such as 7 and 3 or 13 and 7. In this experience, children focus on finding compatible money values totaling 10¢ or 20¢. They may use the bridging-10 strategy for adding numbers such as 9 and 5 by reasoning, for example, that 9 and 1 make 10, plus 4 is 14.

Using the Activities

•••••••••••••••••••••••••••••

1. In Activity 1, children find pairs of stamps that total 10. Ask how they found each sum; for example:

    - "I chose the raccoon and eagle stamps because 7 and 3 is 10."

2. In Activity 2, children find pairs of stamps with a value of 20¢.

3. In Activity 3, the class finds sets of three stamps worth 20¢. The three stamp values in each trio must be different, and no two sets of three stamps can be the same. As each trio is found, cover the three values with counters, and write the trio so that the children can avoid duplicates. When all possible trios have been discovered, all the stamps will have been covered.

Solutions

Activity 3

The 24 trios are:

1, 2, 17	1, 3, 16	1, 4, 15	1, 5, 14	1, 6, 13	1, 7, 12
1, 8, 11	1, 9, 10	2, 3, 15	2, 4, 14	2, 5, 13	2, 6, 12
2, 7, 11	2, 8, 10	3, 4, 13	3, 5, 12	3, 6, 11	3, 7, 10
3, 8, 9	4, 5, 11	4, 6, 10	4, 7, 9	5, 6, 9	5, 7, 8

Extending the Activities

• •

- Name pairs of stamps at random, and ask the children for their total value.

- Challenge children to give the total value of all the stamps in each activity.

- Invite children to create their own sets of stamps for this activity.

What Did I Buy?

Find two stamps worth 10¢.

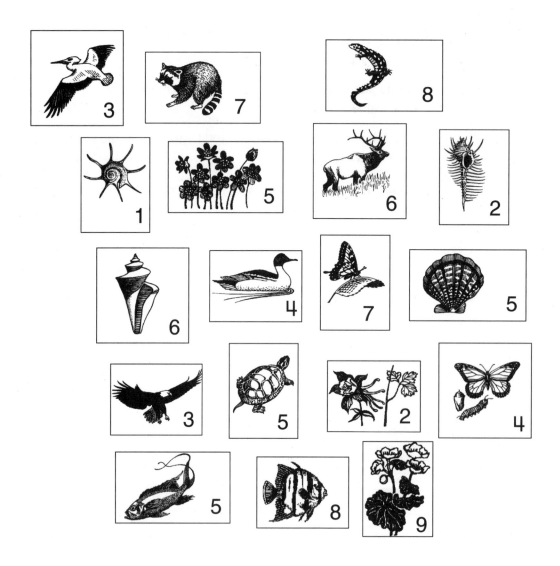

What Did I Buy?

Find two stamps worth 20¢.

What Did I Buy?

Find three stamps worth 20¢.

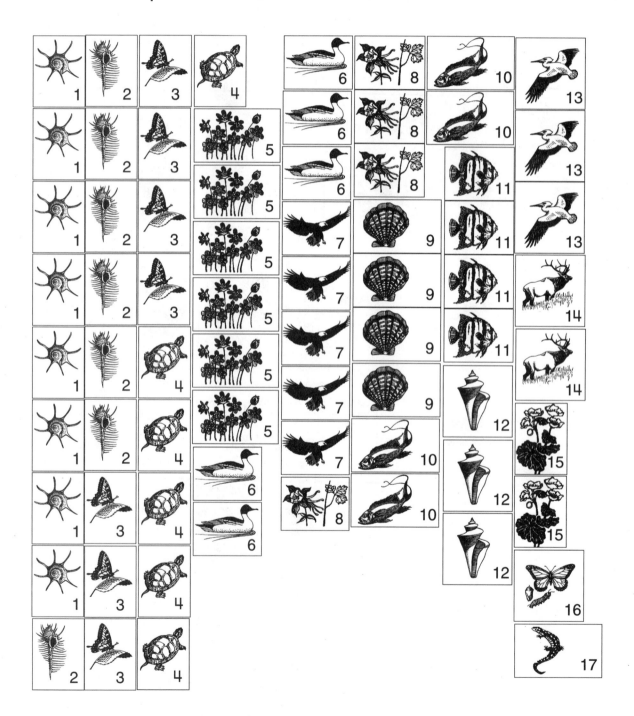

Exploring Multiple Representation

24 is the number of
hours in a day.

24 is 1 less than 25

$$25 - 1 = 24$$

24 is the number of
cans of soda in a case.

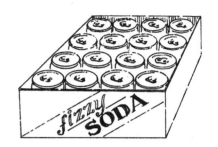

24 is two
dozen eggs.

OOOOOOOOOOOO
OOOOOOOOOOOO

24 is 2 dimes
and 4 pennies.

Numbers may be expressed using a variety of symbolic and graphical representations. For example:

• Four quarters is 10 dimes, 100 pennies, or 1 dollar.

• One hour is 60 minutes.

• The number 8 may be expressed by its word name, the symbol 8, or a drawing:

• The expression $2 + 2 + 2 + 2$ is the same as 4×2.

Understanding multiple representation, recognizing that some representations are more useful than others in certain problem-solving situations, and being able to generate equivalent representations are essential number sense skills.

For example, a person buying something costing $16 could pay with a $20 bill and receive four $1 bills as change. However, it might be neater to pay with a $20 and a $1 bill, and receive a $5 bill as change.

Activities in this section promote several ways to think about equivalent forms of numbers. Experiences in thoughtfully breaking numbers apart—decomposing—and putting them together—recomposing—in different but equivalent ways develop useful skills. The ability to recognize and create different numerical representations that simplify problems is an indication of high-level mathematical thinking.

Every Picture Suggests a Story

Number Sense Focus

• Multiple representation

Mathematical Background

The ability to make sense of quantitative data in pictorial or graphical form is an important skill. Things can be organized visually and in many ways, and each new organization challenges us to interpret what we are seeing.

Using the Activities

1. In Activity 1, children are presented with visual information and are asked to invent situations that the pictures might describe. The emphasis is on realistically interpreting the quantitative information. Show the first picture, and explain that it is showing some information but, because no title or labels are given, we can't tell exactly what the picture is telling us.

2. Invite children to invent a story to go with the graph. Emphasize that the story should contain numbers that fit the picture. Show each of the other pictures, and invite children to share at least two stories to fit each one. For example:

   • "The graph is about the number of pets our class has. There are 4 dogs, 6 cats, 2 birds, and 9 fish."

   • "The graph shows how much money we have saved. I have $5, Aimée has $3, Sean has $4, and Charles has $1."

   • "This is about the weather last week. It rained 1 day, was cloudy 3 days, and was sunny 4 days."

   • "I painted 4 horses and Josh painted 3."

Encourage discussion about the extent to which each story offered fits the visual information and is realistic.

3. The pictures in Activity 2 show things in classifications. Ask children to identify common features of each category, such as, "they are all vegetables." Ask for other things that belong in each category.

4. The pictures in Activity 3 show ways information has been organized. For the first picture, ask the children:

   What is this picture telling us?

   Where would today's date go?

   For the second picture, ask:

   What other things can we ride?

   Where would each go?

   Help the class organize the information in a picture or bar graph by type of vehicle.

Extending the Activities

- Ask children to draw their own graphs and tell stories to accompany them.

- Have children sort a group of objects by different classification schemes.

Every Picture Suggests a Story

Make up a story to fit each picture.

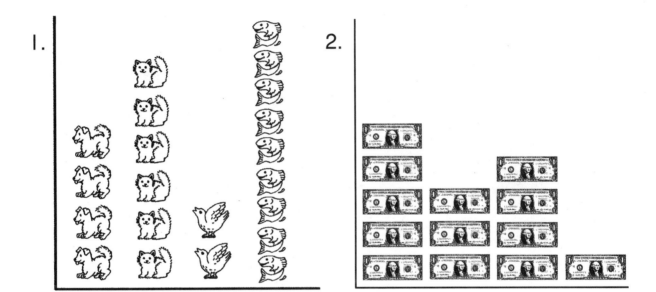

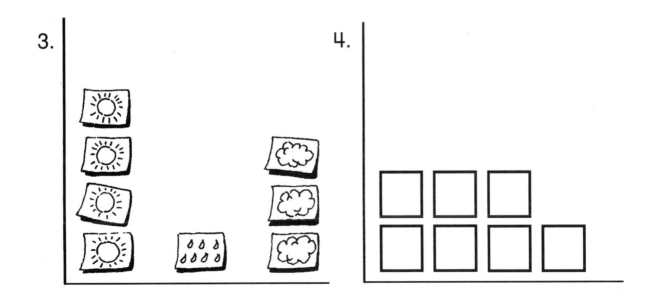

Every Picture Suggests a Story

How are these things grouped?

Name something else that could go in each group.

1.

2.

Number SENSE / Grades 1–2

Every Picture Suggests a Story

What does each picture tell us?

1.

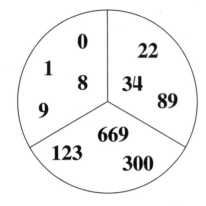

2.

EXPERIENCE 21

Finding Equivalent Sums

Number Sense Focus

- Multiple representation
- Mental computation

Mathematical Background

Recognizing equivalent sums helps us to think flexibly about numbers. For example, knowing that 75¢ + 25¢ is one dollar helps us to recognize that 75 + 25 is 100. Familiarity with compatible numbers promotes mental computation and estimation. It also encourages us to think about numbers and to take advantage of the patterns we observe.

Using the Activities

In these activities, children will find and use equivalent sums that total 100. These activities will stimulate discussion, and they also work well as take-home activities done with the family and later shared with the class.

1. In Activity 1, establish the amount of money on each plate, then ask: Which plate has the most money? the least? Next, ask children to find two plates with coins totaling one dollar and to share how they decided.

2. For Activities 2 and 3, you may want to distribute copies to small groups. In Activity 2, ask children to find as many pairs of numbers as they can that total 50. The grid of cats is a visual illustration of 50 and can be used to help the children find the different pairs. For example, children may choose one number (such as 35), cover up that number of cats, count those remaining (15), and look for that number in the box.

3. In Activity 3, ask the children to find as many pairs of numbers as they can that total 100.

Extending the Activities

- If children are comfortable with Activity 1, offer other challenges. Ask: If the coins on two plates total a dollar and one plate has coins with a total

    - of less than 50¢, what can you say about the total of the other coins?

    - that ends in a 0, what can you say about the coins on the other plate?

    - that ends in a 5, what can you say about the coins on the other plate?

- Have one child place an amount on a desk and ask their partner to decide how much more money is needed to make a dollar.

- Call out a money amount, say $1. Then ask someone to decide how much was spent, say 85¢. Ask: How much change? As children become familiar with this extension, have them call out both the money amount and the amount spent.

- Ask children for other pairs of numbers that total 50 or 100.

Finding Equivalent Sums

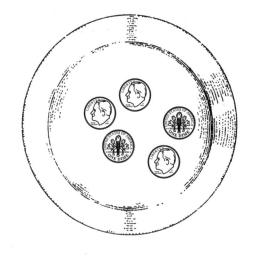

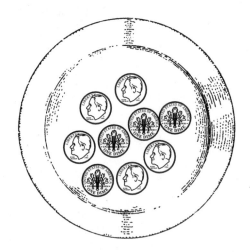

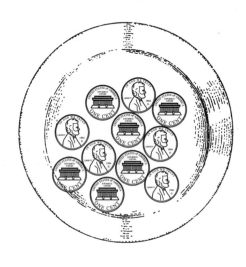

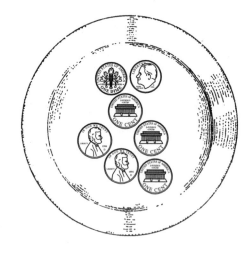

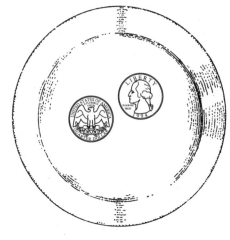

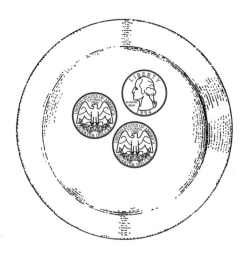

Number SENSE / Grades 1–2

Finding Equivalent Sums

Find pairs that add to 50.

10	25	45	40
5	4	25	48
30	26	20	15
24	2	35	49
46	39	11	1

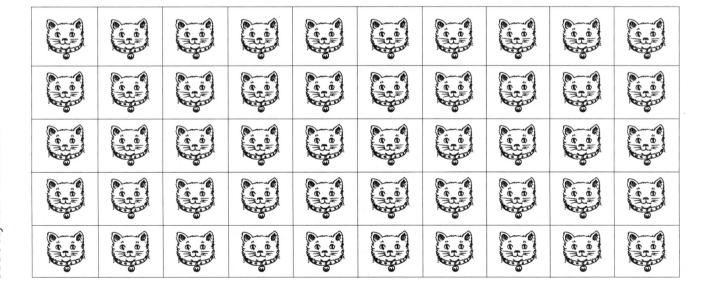

Finding Equivalent Sums

Find pairs that add to 100.

10	25	35	40
5	65	12	88
90	51	20	95
49	2	98	60
89	75	11	80

Number SENSE / Grades 1–2

Making Number Chains

Number Sense Focus

- Multiple representation
- Mental computation

Mathematical Background

Counting and ordering numbers are important early steps in developing number sense. These kinesthetic games encourage children to order numbers in different ways. Children will gain a perspective of multiple representation as they realize, for example, that *two more* for one person is the same as *two fewer* for another person, or that 7 is *2 more than 5* but *2 less than 9*.

Using the Activity

1. To prepare for these games, assign children numbers, starting from 1. Then, have each child design and color a number crown that displays his or her number from the front and back so everyone can see it.

2. As a warm-up, have one child call out a number between 5 and 30. Ask a second child to tell what number is 2 more than the named number, and a third to tell what number is 2 less. For example, if the first child calls out 14, the second child would say 16 and the third 12.

3. Explain the rules for the first game. Let children walk about the room to find the number 2 higher and 2 lower than their number and join hands to form a chain. Once the chains are complete, explore questions such as these:

   - Is everyone holding hands with two different people? Who isn't?

- How does your number compare to the number of the person on your left?

- How does your number compare to the number of the second person on your left?

4. Games 2 and 3 promote further exploration of patterns and relationships. Talk about the results of each game as a class. For example, in Game 1 two lines are formed, one following the sequence 1, 3, 5 and one the sequence 2, 4, 6. In Game 2, three lines are formed. In Game 3, not everyone will find a double, which raises interesting questions:

- Who did not find a double? Why?

- For those without a double, what would your double be?

- Is anyone's double an odd number? Why or why not?

5. In Game 4, children pair up and then try to find numbers they can make with their pairs of numbers. Give each pair some stick-on notes with which to "tag" the numbers they make. For example, 3 and 5 may make 2, 8, or 15: they put a stick-on note on 2's back that says "5 – 3," one on 8's back that says "3 + 5," and one on 15's back that says "3 × 5." After a certain amount of time, or when no more pairs can find other numbers to tag, bring the class back together to look at the tags on each child's back and verify that the calculations are correct.

Extending the Activity

- Help children make up new rules and play the games again. You might change the numbers assigned as well.

Making Number Chains

Game 1

Find the person who is 2 more than you. Take hold of that person's right hand with your left hand.

Game 2

Find the person who is 3 more than you. Take hold of that person's right hand with your left hand.

Game 3

Find the person who is double your number. Take hold of that person's right hand with your left hand.

Game 4

Choose a partner. Now, tag people who have a number that you and your partner can make together.

EXPERIENCE 23

• •

How Could It Happen?

Number Sense Focus

- Multiple representation
- Mental computation

Mathematical Background

• •

There are many ways to represent the same number. For example, 8 − 3 is equivalent to 4 + 1. When children realize that equivalent forms exist, they are more likely to look for and use them.

Using the Activities

• •

In these activities, children construct and generate equivalent relationships.

1. As a warm-up, ask children for different ways to make 6—such as 4 + 2, 10 − 4, 3 + 3, and 2 × 3. Create a list of their suggestions.

2. In each activity, make sure the children understand the rule for combining numbers. Numbers can be subtracted as long as the answer is a whole number. Read each question, and help the class find the possible solutions. Talk about why each solution works.

Solutions

Activity 1

1. 2 + 4, 5 + 1, 3 + 3, or 10 − 4
2. 2 − 1, 3 − 2, 4 − 3, or 5 − 4
3. 3 − 3
4. 10 − 1
5. 0, 1, 2, 3, 4, 5, 6, 7, 8, 9, 11, 13, 14

Activity 2

1. $0 + 7$, $6 + 1$, $4 + 3$, $2 + 5$, $7 - 0$, $8 - 1$, or $9 - 2$
2. Yes; there are ten ways: $9 - 8$, $8 - 7$, $7 - 6$, $6 - 5$, $5 - 4$, $4 - 3$, $3 - 2$, $2 - 1$, $1 - 0$, and $1 + 0$.
3. Any 5 odd numbers between 1 and 17
4. No; there is no way to make an even number in this game. Adding or subtracting an even number and an odd number always produces an odd number.
5. $9 + 8 = 17$

Activity 3

1. $30 + 80$, $40 + 70$, and $50 + 60$
2. Yes; for example, $40 + 10 = 50$ and $60 - 10 = 50$.
3. No, because you cannot make 60 by adding or subtracting an odd and an even multiple of 10.
4. Yes, there are six ways: $40 - 10$, $60 - 30$, $80 - 50$, $70 - 40$, $50 - 20$, and $10 + 20$.
5. Eight: 150, 130, 110, 90, 70, 50, 30, and 10

Activity 4

1. 0, 10, 20, 30, 40
2. 40
3. 3, $0 + 0$, $0 - 0$, $10 - 10$
4. 0, 2, 8, 10, 12, 18, 20, 22, 28, 30, 32, 38, 40
5. 5, 15, 25, 35

Extending the Activities

• •

- Suggest that the children make up mysteries to go with each game. For example: "In Activity 1, Barbara got 8 by adding her numbers and 2 by subtracting them. What could her numbers be?"

- Have the children make their own games, designating the numbers and operations. Then have them write a question related to their game.

How Could It Happen?

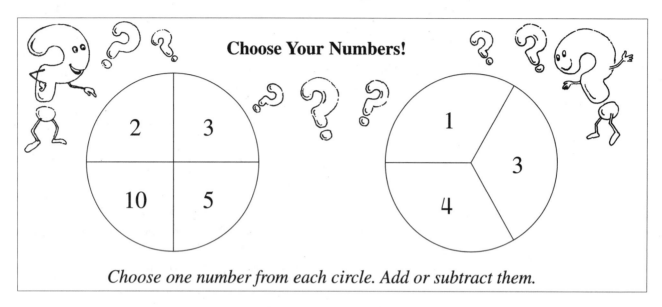

Choose Your Numbers!

Choose one number from each circle. Add or subtract them.

1. Terry chose two numbers and got 6. How did he do it?

2. Leif got 1. How did he do it?

3. Becky got 0. How did she do it?

4. Riki got the largest difference possible. How did he do it?

5. List all the possible results in this game.

How Could It Happen?

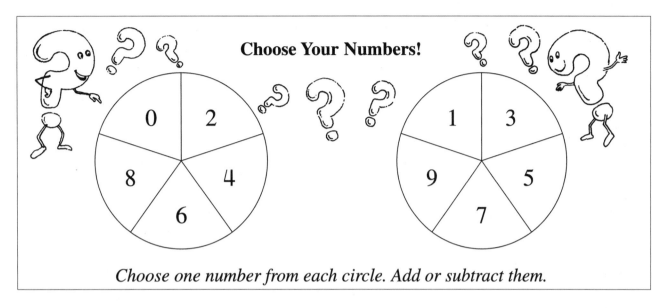

Choose Your Numbers!

Choose one number from each circle. Add or subtract them.

1. Whitney chose two numbers and got 7. How did she do it?

2. Maria says she can make 1 five different ways. Is that possible?

3. List five different numbers you can get in this game.

4. Sara wants to make an even number. Can she? Tell why.

5. What is the largest number you can make?

How Could It Happen?

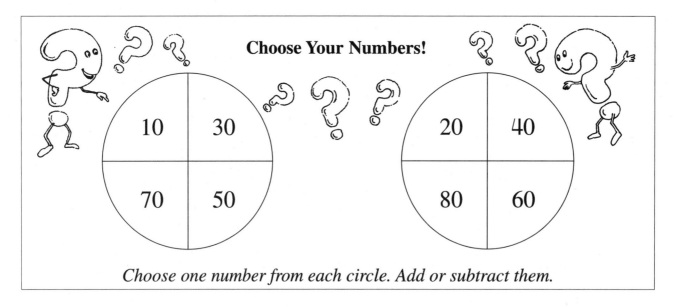

Choose Your Numbers!

10	30
70	50

20	40
80	60

Choose one number from each circle. Add or subtract them.

1. How can you make 110?

2. Can you make 50? Why or why not?

3. Can you make 60? Why or why not?

4. Angel says she can make 30 five different ways. Is that possible? Tell how.

5. How many different numbers can you get?

How Could It Happen?

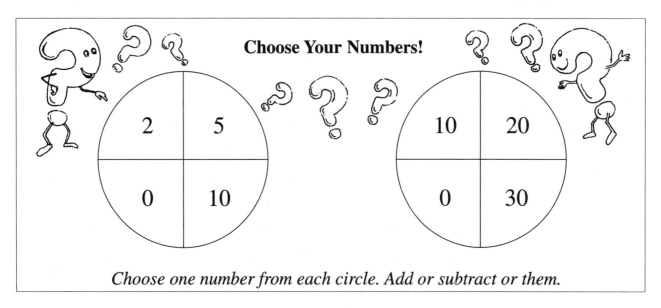

Choose Your Numbers!

| 2 | 5 |
| 0 | 10 |

| 10 | 20 |
| 0 | 30 |

Choose one number from each circle. Add or subtract or them.

1. Sue got an answer that ended in 0. What could her answer be?

2. What is the largest possible answer?

3. How many ways are there to get 0?

4. List all the even results.

5. List all the odd results.

EXPERIENCE 24

Money Amounts

Number Sense Focus

- Multiple representation
- Mental computation

Mathematical Background

Children need to learn to recognize the values of different coins and to understand and apply the relationships among them. The number of ways to represent an amount increases as the value of money increases. There is only one way to represent 1¢, but 5¢ can be represented by 1 nickel or 5 pennies.

Using the Activities

By encouraging children to look for different ways to produce a given amount of money, these activities will help them to begin to recognize the equivalent forms that are encountered regularly when using coins.

1. In Activity 1, ask the children to identify the coins shown. Then, try these activities:

    - Cover up the pennies and nickels. Ask: What coins can you see? How much money is this?

    - Cover up the dimes and pennies. Ask: What coins can you see? How much money is this?

    - Cover up the dimes and nickels. Ask: What coins can you see? How much money is this?

    - Say: Suppose you picked two coins. What is the most money you could get? the least?

2. In Activity 2, ask children to identify the coins. Then, ask how they could pick out 25¢ (for example, 5 pennies and 2 dimes or 3 nickels and 1 dime). Make a list of their ideas, then ask: Which of these would be the easiest to carry in your hand? Why?

3. In Activity 3, ask children how they could pick out $1 (for example, 2 quarters and 5 dimes or 10 nickels and 5 dimes). Again, list their answers, then ask which combination would be the easiest to carry.

Extending the Activities

• •

- Show one of the collections of coins, and ask: Suppose I pick up three (four) of these coins. How much money could I have? What is the most? the least?

- Ask children to figure out how many different combinations of coins equal half a dollar.

Money Amounts

What 2 coins will give me the most money?

Number SENSE / Grades 1–2

Money Amounts

Money Amounts

I want $1.

Number SENSE / Grades 1–2

Number This Name

Number Sense Focus

- Multiple representation
- Relative size

Mathematical Background

Just as knowing the names for animals is important for identifying and discussing them, knowing common number names helps us communicate mathematical ideas. Mathematical concepts are encountered in many settings, but the appropriate terms must eventually be connected to the concepts to harness their full power. For example, as children become familiar with the concept of triangles and explore their properties (three sides and three angles), it is helpful for them to connect the prefix *tri* with other words, such as *tricycle*. Recognizing common prefixes provides useful clues to word meanings.

Using the Activities

In these activities, the class explores everyday mathematical vocabulary.

1. In Activity 1, ask children to match each picture with a word and a number. Help them understand the meanings of the words if they are unfamiliar with them.

2. In Activity 2, again help children match each picture with a word and a number. Then, talk about the prefixes *uni, bi,* and *tri* and their meanings (1, 2, and 3).

Extending the Activities

• •

- Ask the children to tell a short story using some of the new words in a meaningful way.

- Talk to the children about other number prefixes. For example, *octo,* as in *octopus,* means 8.

Number This Name

4

quintuplets

twins

2

triplets

3

quadruplets

5

Number This Name

unicycle

2

3

tricycle

unicorn

1

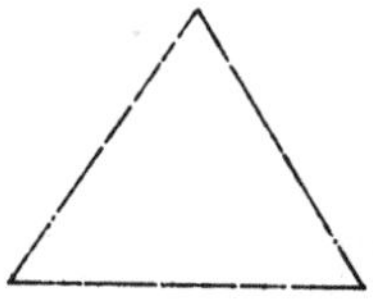

bilingual

triangle

bicycle

Number SENSE / Grades 1–2

Exploring Number Relationships

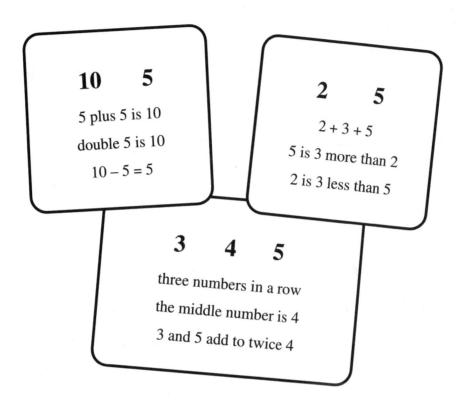

Every number is related to other numbers in many ways. The recognition of multiple relationships among numbers is one of the hallmarks of people with good number sense. In mental computation, the numbers 10 or 100 are particularly useful, as are compatible numbers.

Recognizing relationships among numbers often makes a calculation simpler. For example, we can reason about 8 + 9 in many ways:

- 8 + 9 is the same as 8 + 8 + 1, which is 17.

- Two 9s is 18, and minus 1 is 17.

- 10 plus 10 is 20; then take away 2 and take away 1 is 17.

The greater the number of relationships among numbers that are recognized, the greater the number of choices that are available.

Number relationships are also used in estimation. For example, noticing the relationship between each number and 50 makes it possible to estimate 47 + 49 as less than 100 easily and confidently. Relationships also exist among sequences of numbers. For example, 2, 4, 6, 8, . . . and 2, 4, 8, 16, . . . are two forms of growth that demonstrate regular relationships between successive numbers. Recognizing such patterns helps us to identify trends and regularities in data and to notice when a number seems to be out of place because it does not fit the pattern.

These activities encourage children to explore number relationships and to take advantage of the relationships they observe.

Addition and Subtraction Connections

Number Sense Focus

- Number relationships
- Mental computation

Mathematical Background

When we compute mentally, we constantly discover and use relationships among numbers. For example, when adding 7 and 5, we may think of 5 as $3 + 2$ and so calculate $(7 + 3) + 2$.

Using the Activities

These activities encourage children to spot addition and subtraction connections among sets of three numbers. Many relationships exist for each set of numbers in this experience.

1. The numbers in Activity 1 lend themselves to simple addition and subtraction relationships, such as $1 + 3 = 4$, $6 + 3 = 9$, and $7 - 5 = 2$. Show the first group of numbers, and invite children to choose three numbers to connect. Offer an example of your own.

2. Ask individuals to name their three numbers and give a relationship. Ask whether other children connected the same numbers in a different way. Make a list of the relationships, and add more as children offer them. For example:

$1 + 2 = 3$	$1 + 3 = 4$	$1 + 4 = 5$
$2 + 3 = 5$	$2 + 5 = 7$	$3 + 4 = 7$
$3 - 2 = 1$	$3 + 4 = 7$	$7 - 2 = 5$

3. Activities 2 and 3 involve one- and two-digit numbers. Use them in the same way.

Extending the Activities

• •

- Give children two or three minutes to find as many connections as they can among sets of three numbers in a given group of numbers.

- Ask children to create a set of 10 numbers with many interesting relationships. You may wish to include multiplication.

- Challenge children to find as many ways as they can to get from one given number to another. For example, starting at 2 and ending at 10 could be done in these ways:

$$2 + 1 + 7 = 10 \qquad 2 + 3 + 5 = 10$$
$$2 + 9 - 1 = 10 \qquad 2 + 7 - 4 + 5 = 10$$

Addition and Subtraction Connections

Addition and Subtraction Connections

7   13   5

8

15

2

10   18

3

12

Find 3 numbers.

Connect them with + or – and =.

11

9   2   12

16

23   18

5   7

14

Addition and Subtraction Connections

7   11   13   3

18   25   14

4   21   24

10

Find 3 numbers.

Connect them with + or – and =.

_____

13   8

89   5   3

21

55

34

2   1

EXPERIENCE 27

• •

What Number Am I?

Number Sense Focus

- Number relationships
- Multiple representation

Mathematical Background

• •

Every number can be described in many ways. For example, 7 is 3 + 4, a prime number, the number of days in a week, and two pennies and a nickel. Part of good number sense is recognizing different ways of expressing numbers and their characteristics.

Using the Activities

• •

In these activities, children are asked to name a whole number satisfying certain clues.

1. As a warm-up, ask the children to tell you some things about the number 5. For example, it is less than 7, it is odd, it is more than 4, and it equals 3 + 2. Create a list of their ideas.

2. Put the children in teams of two or four. Read the clues for the first puzzle in Activity 1 aloud. Make sure the children realize that the answer can be 1, 10, or any whole number in between. Ask that each team agree on an answer for the set of clues and be ready to explain it.

3. Let the teams share their answers. Some of the clues in the puzzles are not needed; you might ask teams to identify the unnecessary clues and tell why they are not needed. All the clues in Activity 1 are "more than" or "less than." Activity 2 has more varied clues. Activity 3 involves numbers from 1 to 20.

Solutions

Activity 1

1. 4   2. 2   3. 7   4. 1   5. 6   6. 5

Activity 2

1. 5   2. 3   3. 8   4. 6   5. 4   6. 9

Activity 3

1. 10   2. 12   3. 15   4. 18   5. 13   6. 7

Extending the Activities

- Have teams make up their own number puzzles and exchange them.

What Number Am I?

1. I am more than 2.
   I am less than 7.
   I am more than 3.
   I am less than 5.
   What number am I?

2. I am less than 8.
   I am more than 1.
   I am less than 5.
   I am less than 3.
   What number am I?

3. I am more than 3.
   I am less than 9.
   I am more than 6.
   I am less than 8.
   What number am I?

4. I am more than 0.
   I am less than 4.
   I am less than 5.
   I am less than 2.
   What number am I?

5. I am more than 3.
   I am less than 8.
   I am more than 5.
   I am less than 7.
   What number am I?

6. I am more than 2.
   I am less than 7.
   I am more than 4.
   I am less than 6.
   What number am I?

Number SENSE / Grades 1–2

What Number Am I?

1. I am more than 2.
   I am odd.
   I am less than 7.
   I am half of 10.
   What number am I?

2. I am less than 7.
   I am odd.
   I am the number of mice
      in a famous rhyme.
   What number am I?

3. I am not less than 5.
   I am even.
   I am not twice 3.
   I do not have two digits.
   What number am I?

4. I am not 2.
   I am not odd.
   I am not less than 5.
   I am not more than 7.
   What number am I?

5. I am even.
   If you double me,
   I am still less than 10.
   I am twice an even number.
   What number am I?

6. I am more than 5.
   I am odd.
   I am not the number
      of days in a week.
   What number am I?

What Number Am I?

1. I am 2 times a number.
   I am less than 15.
   I am 5 times a number.
   What number am I?

2. I am even.
   I have two digits.
   One digit is twice the other.
   What number am I?

3. I am odd.
   I am 5 times a number.
   My digits add to 6.
   What number am I?

4. I am 3 times a number.
   I am more than 10.
   My digits add to 9.
   What number am I?

5. I am more than 10.
   I am odd.
   My digits add to 4.
   What number am I?

6. I am less than 12.
   I am odd.
   Twice my number has a 4 in it.
   What number am I?

My Two Numbers

Number Sense Focus

- Number relationships
- Mental computation

Mathematical Background

Children need experiences to learn that many numbers may share a given relationship and that multiple connections exist among numbers. They must also learn that questions sometimes have many answers.

Using the Activities

In these activities, children must choose two numbers that have a given relationship. There are many possibilities for every question, students can work together as a class to find as many as possible.

1. Introduce the activity by choosing two numbers (such as, 2 and 3) and asking children to say something about them.

   - They differ by 1.

   - They add to 5.

   - One is even, the other odd.

   Show statement 1 of Activity 1. Explain to the children they are looking for two numbers that fit the statement. Ask them to write the numbers down. Ask children to state their two numbers and keep a list of all the different possibilities.

2. Show each relationship in turn, and use the same procedure: have the children write down their two numbers then state them. You can also ask each child to think to more than one pair of numbers to match the statement or have small groups work together to find several pairs of numbers.

3. Use Activity 2 in the same way.

Extending the Activities

- Some of the statements can be made more specific by adding a phrase such as, "under thirty."

- Invite children to challenge the class with a relationship they have thought of.

- Have groups of children make up a set of relationships.

- State a relationship, and give children 30 seconds to write as many numbers as they can that share that relationship.

My Two Numbers

My two numbers

1. are both even.

2. add to 10.

3. add to 14.

4. differ by 1.

5. differ by 4.

6. are both less than 10.

7. are both between 10 and 20.

8. both have a 3 in them.

My Two Numbers

My two numbers

1. differ by 20.

2. add to 20.

3. are both between 5 and 15.

4. have a 2 in the ones place.

5. are both odd.

6. are both years before I was born.

7. both have a 0 in them.

8. differ by 100.

Finding Triplets

Number Sense Focus

- Number relationships
- Mental computation

Mathematical Background

The ability to recognize and move among equivalent forms of the same number is a sign of good number sense.

Using the Activities

Each activity consists of 15 boxes labeled A to O, each containing a number or an expression. The task is to group the boxes into five groups of three, each group containing equivalent numbers or expressions (for example, 15, 5×3, and $20 - 5$).

1. In Activity 1, draw the children's attention to the box labeled M, and ask: What number is in box M? *(1)* Can anyone see other boxes worth 1? *(Yes, box J and box F.)* Boxes F, J, and M belong together because they are all worth 1. Can you find other sets of three boxes that are all worth the same? Cover the sets of boxes with counters as they are found.

2. Do the activities as a class, or make copies of the activities so children can work individually or in pairs to find the sets of three boxes. You may wish to draw their attention to each of the other boxes that contain a single digit (B, C, E, and K) one at a time, and have them find the two equivalent boxes. If they are ready, let them sort the remaining 12 boxes at once, recording the sets of three letters as they do so.

3. Use Activities 2 and 3 in the same way.

Solutions

Activity 1

F, J, M (1); A, B, L (4); G, I, K (5); C, D, N (6); E, H, O (7)

Activity 2

E, O, J (11); C, G, K (12); B, F, M (13); D, H, I (14); A, L, N (15)

Activity 3

D, H, I (16); A, L, N (17); B, F, M (18); E, O, J (19); C, G, K (20)

Extending the Activities

• •

- Have children create their own sets of boxes for others to sort.

- Make a 5×5 grid of squares with five sets of five equivalent expressions, and invite the children to sort them.

- Let children use counters to cover the squares and play concentration.

Finding Triplets

Find three boxes that are equal.

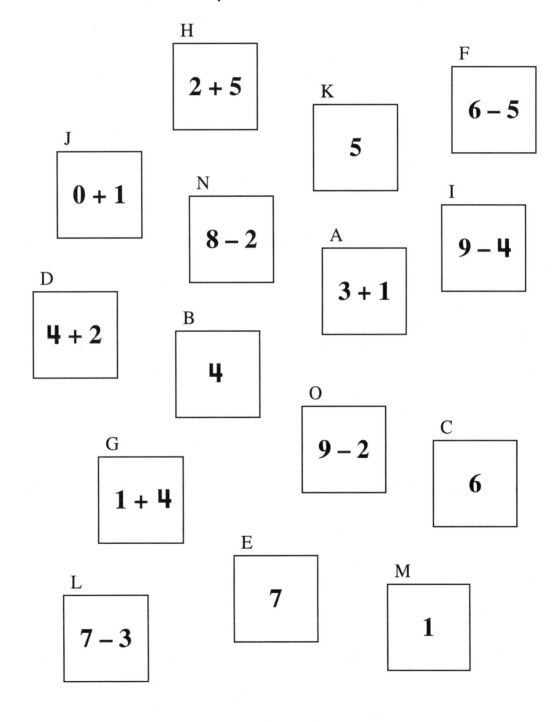

H
2 + 5

K
5

F
6 – 5

J
0 + 1

N
8 – 2

I
9 – 4

A
3 + 1

D
4 + 2

B
4

O
9 – 2

C
6

G
1 + 4

E
7

M
1

L
7 – 3

Finding Triplets

Find three boxes that are equal.

H

14

K

17 – 5

F

10 + 3

J

11

N

20 – 5

A

3 + 12

I

9 + 5

D

16 –2

B

13

O

4 + 7

C

12

G

9 + 3

E

6 + 5

M

17 – 4

L

15

Finding Triplets

Find three boxes that are equal.

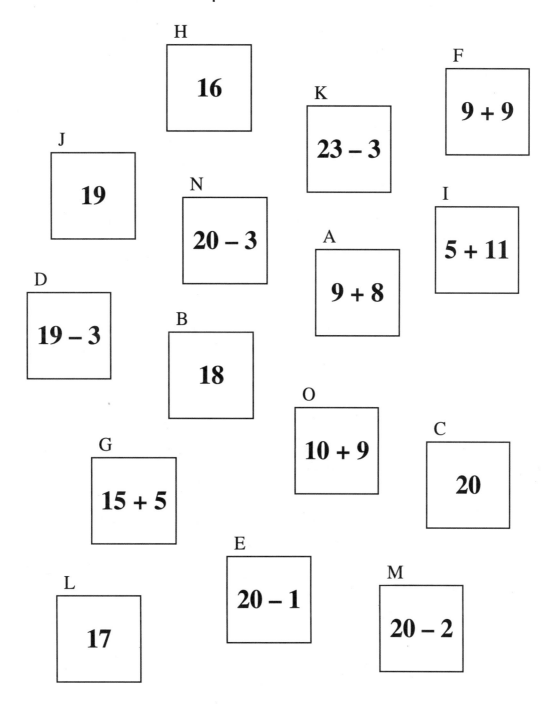

H
16

F
9 + 9

K
23 – 3

J
19

N
20 – 3

I
5 + 11

A
9 + 8

D
19 – 3

B
18

O
10 + 9

C
20

G
15 + 5

E
20 – 1

M
20 – 2

L
17

EXPERIENCE 30

From Here to There

Number Sense Focus

- Number relationships

Mathematical Background

Any pair of numbers can be related by an addition or a subtraction. The ability to recognize and express a variety of relationships among numbers is a sign of good number sense.

Using the Activities

These activities invite children to explore connections between two numbers.

1. In Activity 1, show only the 3 and the + 4 at the top of the ring, and ask children what number they expect to see in the next circle. Reveal the 7 and then the – 6, and ask what number they expect to see next. Proceed around the circle.

2. In Activity 2, show the ring and ask what should go in the circle after + 5. Invite children to share how they worked this out. Proceed around the circle.

3. In Activity 3, show the ring and ask the children what is missing. *(the numbers on the arrows)* Start with the 12, and ask children how they could turn it into 3—what would they have to add or subtract? Encourage the use of counters, calculators, and mental calculation. Proceed around the circle.

Extending the Activities

• •

- Give the children copies of Activity 2. Ask them to replace the 10 at the top with another number and then fill in the other circles.

- The children can make and exchange their own rings, putting numbers either on the arrows or in the circles and supplying answers on the back. (If they put numbers on the arrows, the sum of the numbers added must equal the sum of the numbers subtracted. The easiest way to ensure this is to start by putting numbers in the circles as they go around and then erase them when the numbers on the arrows have been determined.)

From Here to There

What comes next?

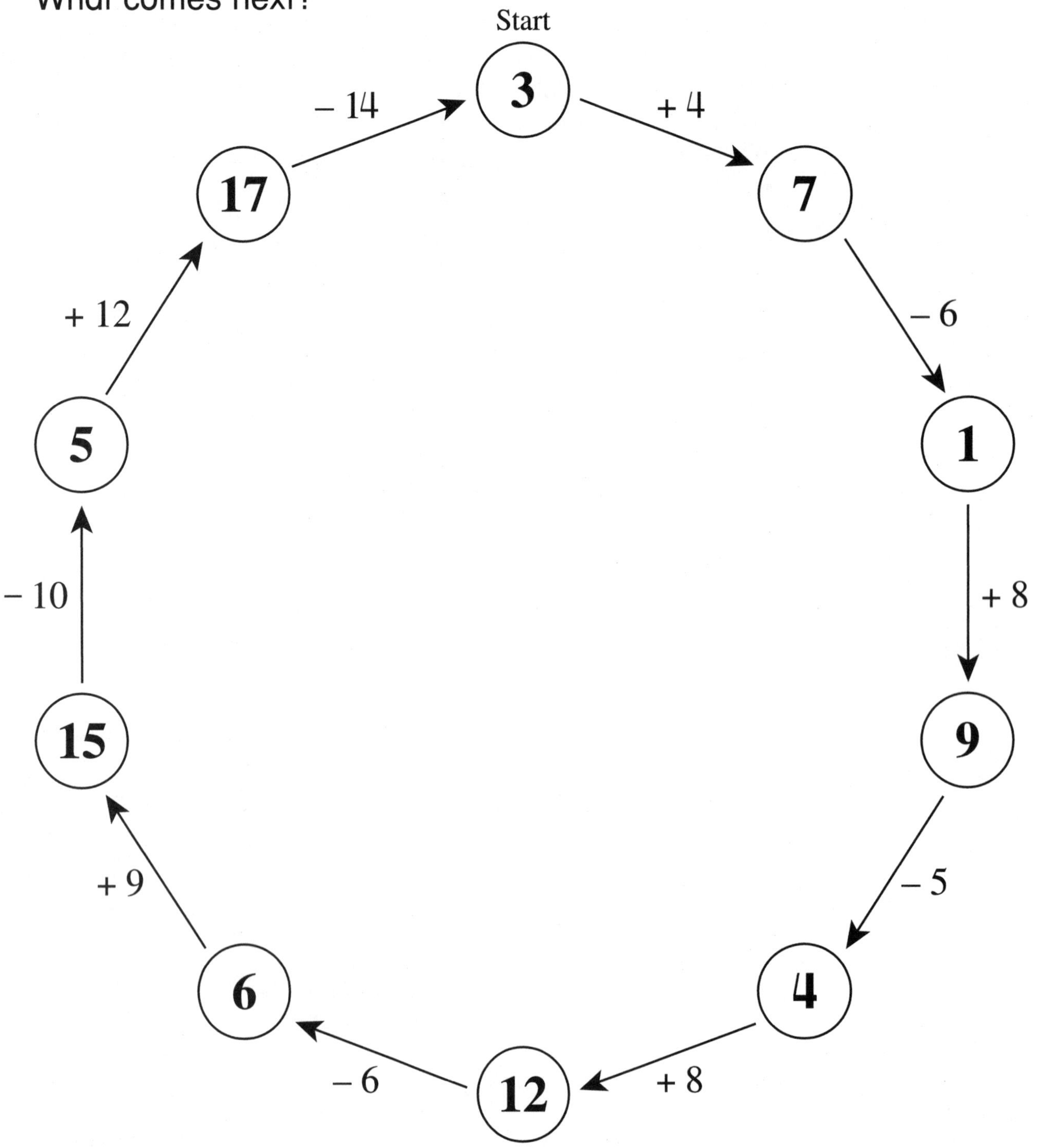

Start

3

− 14   + 4

17   7

+ 12   − 6

5   1

− 10   + 8

15   9

+ 9   − 5

6   4

− 6   + 8

12

©Dale Seymour Publications®

From Here to There

What numbers go in the circles?

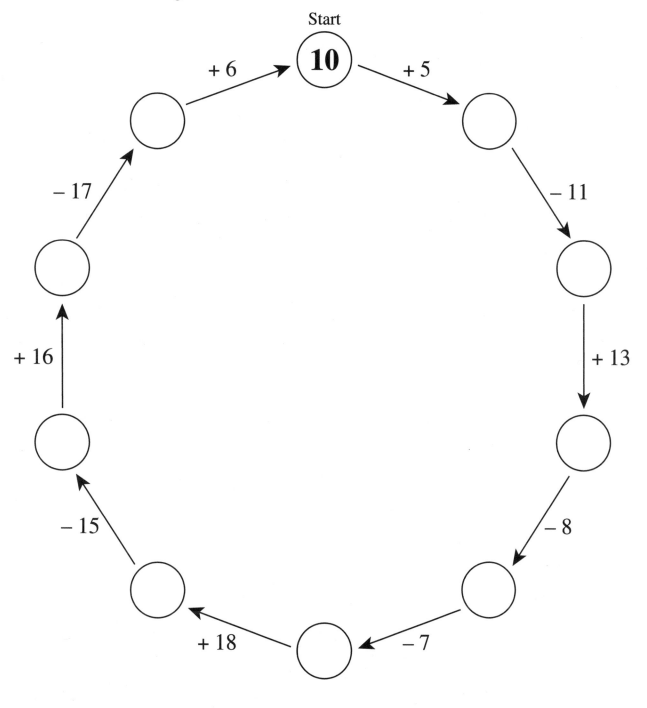

From Here to There

What belongs on the arrows?

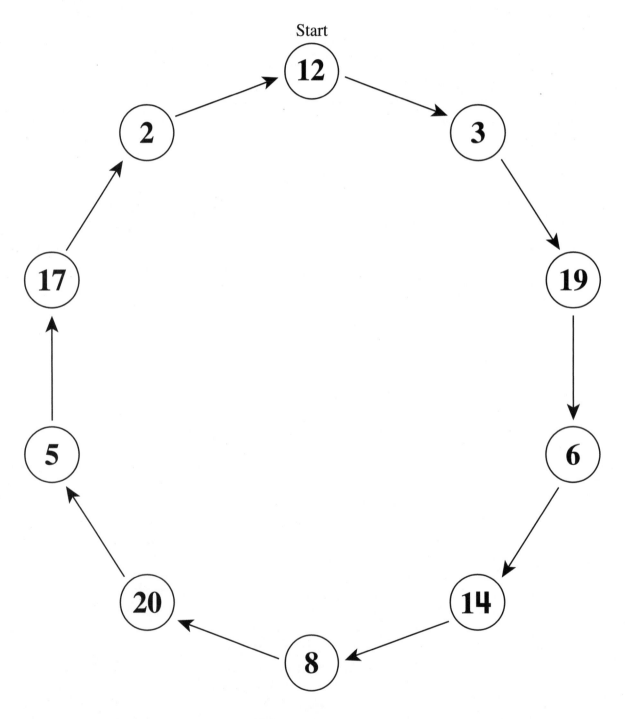

Start

Number SENSE / Grades 1–2

Exploring Relative Size

An awareness of the relative size of numbers requires a knowledge of strategies for relating the sizes of numbers, but it also involves personal judgment and decision making. For example, is A.D. 1800 relatively recent? A scholar of ancient history would likely answer this question differently from a scholar of contemporary history. In terms of a human life span, 1980 is very recent to some people and ancient history to others. Personal knowledge, experience, and judgment are reflected in any decision about the relative size of numbers.

An understanding of the relative size of whole numbers depends on an understanding of place value. Reversals of digits, such as 39 and 93, are often confusing to children in reading and writing values, even though the quantities represented by the symbols are easy to distinguish. Experiences that help connect these symbols to concrete models in meaningful ways are essential to developing number sense.

Children can gain additional insight into the relative size of numbers by recognizing and using benchmarks such as 10, 20, 50, and 100. While it may not be possible to determine the exact number of objects in a group near a benchmark such as 50 without counting, it is helpful to be able to place the quantity near a benchmark without tedious counting. Many important ideas about relative size of numbers can be established in these ways.

Doubling Numbers

Number Sense Focus

- Relative size
- Measurement
- Estimation

Mathematical Background

The concept of doubling is important both mathematically and in everyday situations; for example, many games call for us to double numbers mentally. The impact of doubling can be dramatic when the results are expressed visually.

Using the Activities

These activities offer visual models of doubled numbers that promote thinking about the relative size of numbers.

1. As a warm-up, have a child name a number between 1 and 5, then ask the children to double that number. If a child names 4, you might ask four children to stand on one side of the room and double that number to stand on the other side. Encourage children to tell ways they can decide if double the number are standing. Though the children may not have formally been introduced to multiplication, doubling is a natural process, and creative solutions will likely be suggested.

2. In Activity 1, show the transparency, point to a bar, and ask: Which bar is double the length of this one? Discuss ways of deciding this by inspection. Repeat for each of bars A–D. Ask: Do you need to know the length of a bar to know its double? *(No; it is possible to tell by sight which bar is about double another.)*

3. Measure the bars to verify the doubles, either using a transparent centimeter ruler on the overhead, or projecting the transparency on a wall and having the children measure the bars. Help them discover that the lengths depend on the distance of the projector from the wall and on the measuring instrument used, but that the numbers will always indicate the doubles. You might ask children the length of the bar that would be double the longest bar, and why this bar isn't on the transparency. *(It would be too long to fit.)*

4. In Activity 2, point to a "snake string" and follow a similar procedure. To help children measure the snake strings, you may want to place a transparency of 1-centimeter dot paper over the activity sheet. Children might suggest other strategies for determining which snake strings are doubles.

5. In Activity 3, point to a curved "snake string" and follow a similar procedure. The curves will make measuring more difficult but encourage the children to make visual judgments.

Solutions

The lengths of the items on the activity sheets are given here.

Activity 1

B—1 cm, D—2 cm, A—4 cm, C—8 cm, E—16 cm

Activity 2

B—1 cm, G—2 cm, D—4 cm, A—8 cm, C—16 cm, E—32 cm, F—64 cm

Activity 3

C—1 cm, B—2 cm, D—4 cm, A—8 cm, E—16 cm, F—32 cm, G—64 cm

Extending the Activities

• •

- Take a sheet of paper. Have another child take two sheets, the next child four sheets, and so on until the children realize how quickly doubled numbers increase.

- Have children cut a short piece of string, then a second double the length of the first, and continue for 8 or 10 pieces. Help them make a "Doubling" poster by gluing the strings onto poster board and labeling them with their length.

- If children are ready, reuse the transparencies and talk about halving numbers.

Doubling Numbers

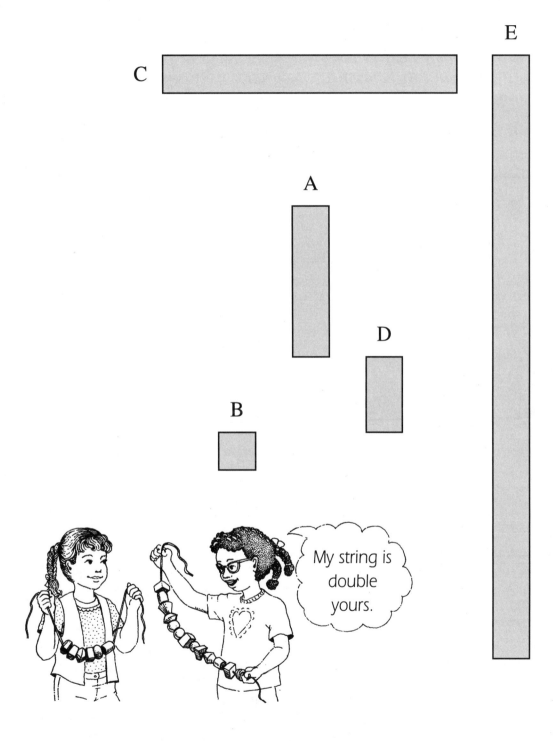

My string is double yours.

Doubling Numbers

A ——————————————

G ————

C ——

B ——

D ————

E ——————————————————————

F ——————————————

Help me find a double.

Doubling Numbers

EXPERIENCE 32

• •

Number Amounts

Number Sense Focus

• Relative size
• Estimation

Mathematical Background

• •

A feeling for the size of numbers develops over a lifetime. For most of us, millions, billions, and trillions are difficult to comprehend. For young children, smaller numbers may be equally incomprehensible. Developing benchmarks is a fundamental step in appreciating the relative size of numbers.

Using the Activities

• •

1. In Activity 1, ask children: Which square has the greatest number of stars in it? the least? Ask them to order the squares from greatest to least. Here are several options to encourage them to think about the number of stars in the boxes:

   • Focus on one box, and have the children guess the number of stars in it. After each guess, you—or a child who knows the exact amount—could provide clues, such as "too high," "too low," or "not quite enough." Continue until the number is identified.

   • Show all the boxes. Tell children the number of stars in one of the boxes (5, 10, 50, or 100), and ask them which box it is and how they know.

   • Show all four boxes and the numbers at the bottom of the page, and ask children to match the numbers with the boxes.

2. Use Activity 2 in the same way.

3. Activity 3 focuses on the relative sizes of reversed digits, such as 19 and 91. Show each pair of boxes and ask: Which has more (fewer)? Then identify the number pairs that go with the boxes, and ask children to match them. The children will realize that some pairs are easier to distinguish (such as 19 and 91) than others (45 and 54).

Extending the Activities

- Have children make a poster with useful benchmarks, such as 10, 20, 50, and 100.

- Have children create a poster displaying numbers with reversed digits, such as 17 and 71 or larger numbers such as 103 and 301 or 1003 and 3001.

Number Amounts

5   10   50   100

Number Amounts

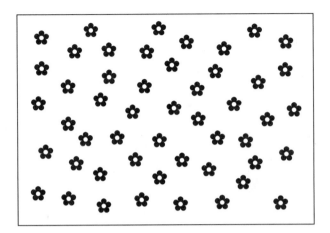
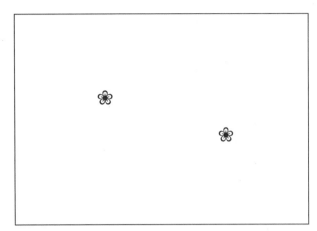
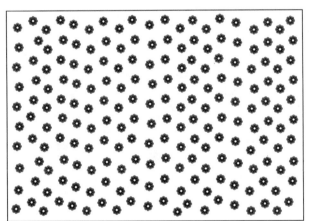
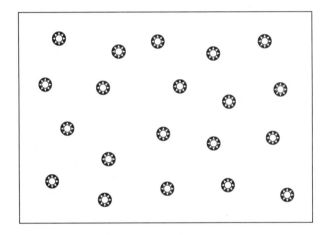
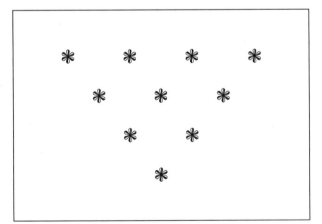

2 10 20 50 100 200

Number Amounts

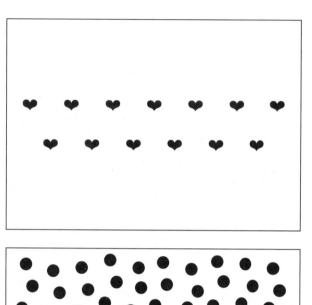
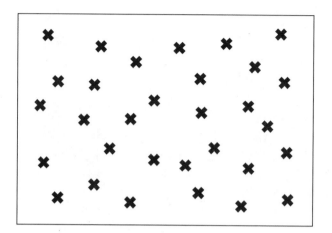
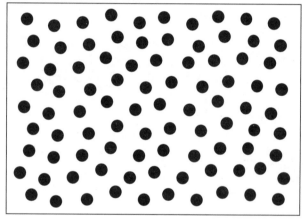
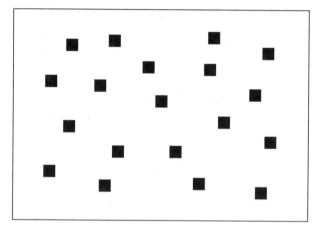

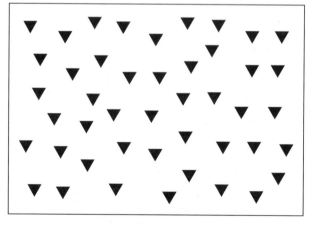

19   91   54   45   13   31

Number SENSE / Grades 1–2

Pick a Word

Number Sense Focus

- Relative size

Mathematical Background

Developing vocabulary is an important part of working with numbers. Talking with children about words in ways that are natural and meaningful for them helps promote greater understanding.

Using the Activities

In these activities, children decide what key questions specific words and phrases are associated with: How many? (which focuses on quantity), Where? (which focuses on position or ordinal relationship), and When? (which focuses on time).

1. Show Activity 1. Point to words or phrases, and use each in a sentence: The party will be today. The moon can be seen in the evening. Jean's grandparents live far away. Ask the children what the phrase tells us: where, how many, or when.

2. Ask the children to choose a word or phrase, use it in a sentence, and tell in which box it belongs. It is possible to place some of the words and phrases into more than one box. The focus should be on explaining *why* a phrase belongs in a particular box in a given context.

3. Use Activities 2 and 3 in a similar way.

Extending the Activities

- Ask children to suggest other words and phrases that belong in each box.

Pick a Word

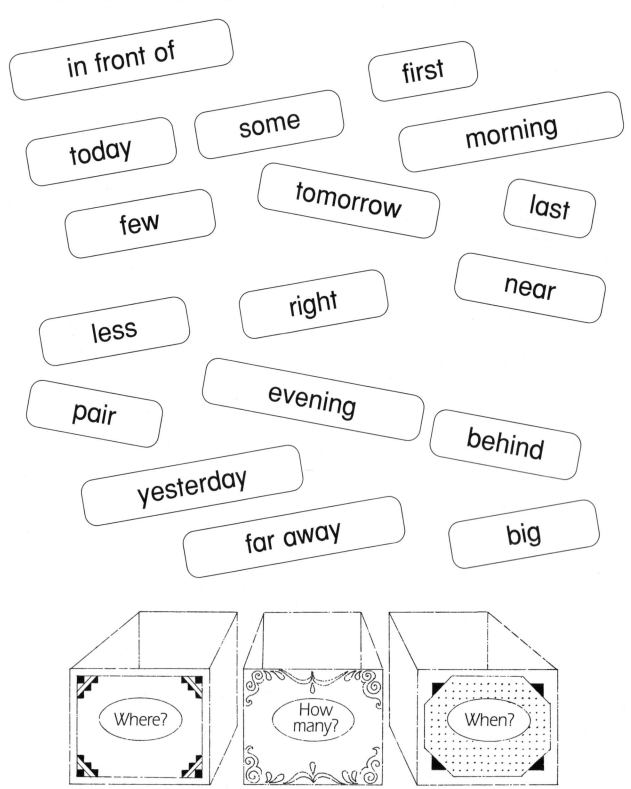

in front of

first

today

some

morning

tomorrow

last

few

near

less

right

pair

evening

behind

yesterday

far away

big

Where?

How many?

When?

Pick a Word

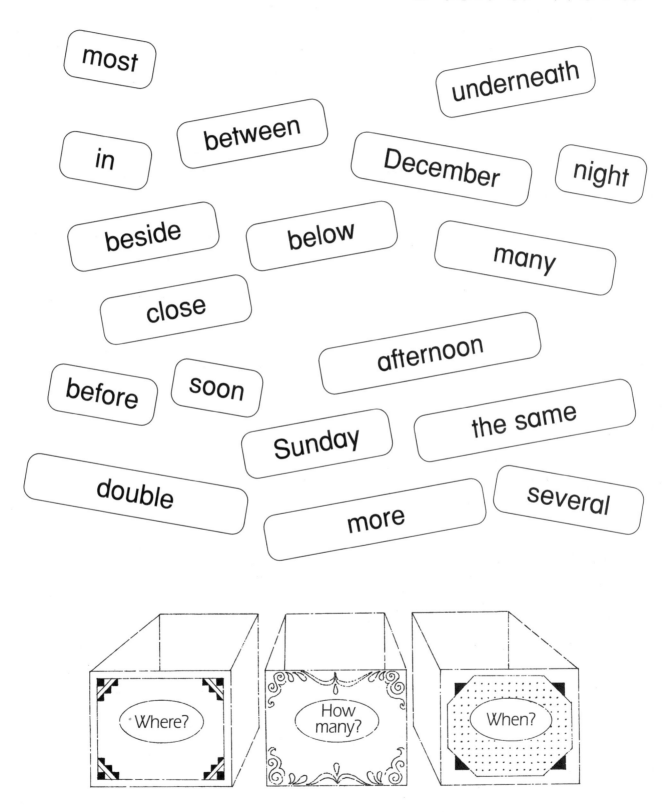

most

underneath

between

in

December

night

beside

below

many

close

afternoon

before

soon

Sunday

the same

double

more

several

Where?

How many?

When?

Pick a Word

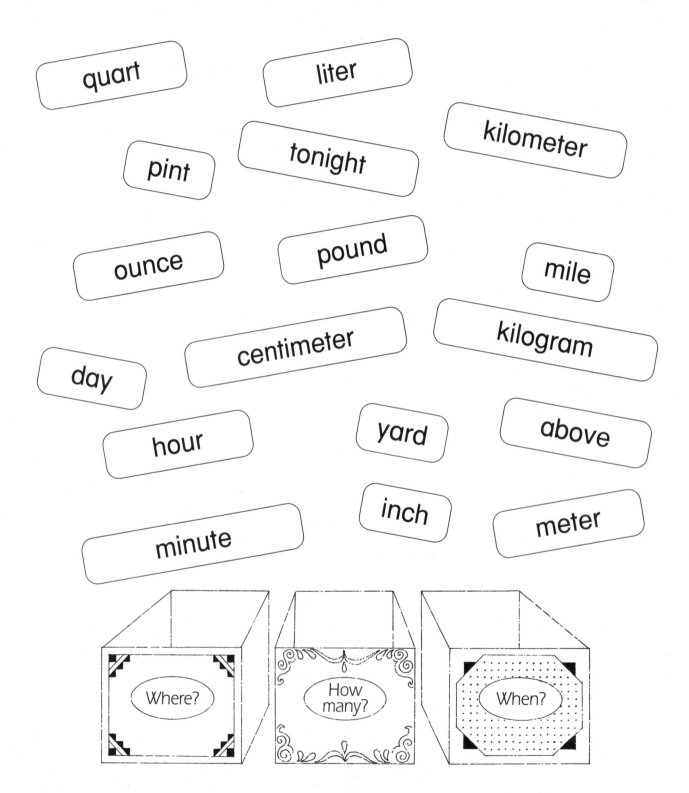

quart

liter

pint

tonight

kilometer

ounce

pound

mile

day

centimeter

kilogram

hour

yard

above

inch

meter

minute

Where?

How many?

When?

Number SENSE / Grades 1–2